D0810301

AUTOBIOGRAPHICAL NOTES

by

I. M. Sechenov

Editor of English Translation
DONALD B. LINDSLEY

Translated from the Russian by
KRISTAN HANES

Published by
AMERICAN INSTITUTE OF BIOLOGICAL SCIENCES
and Co-Sponsored by
AMERICAN PSYCHOLOGICAL ASSOCIATION
WASHINGTON, D. C.

Library of Congress Catalog Card Number 65-16726

Copyright 1965

AMERICAN INSTITUTE OF BIOLOGICAL SCIENCES
3900 Wisconsin Avenue, Washington, D.C. 20016

PRINTED IN THE UNITED STATES OF AMERICA BY
GARAMOND/PRIDEMARK PRESS, BALTIMORE, MARYLAND

ACADEMY OF MEDICAL SCIENCES, USSR

Series on Outstanding Men in Russian Medicine

I. M. Sᴇᴄʜᴇɴᴏᴠ

AUTOBIOGRAPHICAL NOTES

PUBLISHING HOUSE OF THE ACADEMY OF MEDICAL SCIENCES USSR

Moscow 1952

Portrait of Sechenov, 1889, by Repin

EDITOR'S PREFACE

Sechenov, revered as the father of physiology in Russia, was born in the south of Russia in the village of Teplyy Stan, on August 1, 1829. His initial training was as an engineer in the Military Engineering School, but he did not like engineering and turned instead to Medicine and Physiology. From 1843 to 1850 he was in training as an engineer; from 1850 to 1856 he was at Moscow University for his medical and scientific training in physiology. From 1856 to 1860 he went abroad to study and was fortunate to have been permitted to work in the laboratories of some of the most outstanding men in his field of that day, namely, Emil du Bois-Reymond, Carl Ludwig, and Claude Bernard. He also came into association with other great minds such as those of Johannes Müller, Hermann von Helmholtz, and Hoppe-Seyler, to mention only a few.

Subsequently he returned to Russia to establish laboratories at the universities of Petersburg (Leningrad), Odessa and Moscow. His scientific and academic pursuits, although always stimulating and challenging were fraught with difficulties due to political interference and harassment. But he continued in teaching and research for forty years.

These Autobiographical Notes provide a warm, intimate, and vivid picture of Sechenov's history, written about a year before his death on November 2, 1905.

FOREWORD

This is the second of a series of translations of Russian Monographs on brain and behavior, concentrating upon the historical background of investigations in neurophysiology and conditioned behavior as well as upon certain contemporary advances in these fields.

The translation program was initiated by H. W. Magoun and D. B. Lindsley and has been continued by the latter. It has been supported by U. S. Public Health Service grant NB-02347. Grateful acknowledgement is made to the publisher, the American Institute of Biological Sciences, and to Tom Wheaton Coward, Manager of Publications for facilitating the preparations of publication.

Thanks are due also to Kristan Hanes, translator, and to Helen B. Wiczenski, typist and coordinator, for their persistent and devoted efforts.

DONALD B. LINDSLEY
Professor of Psychology and Physiology
University of California, Los Angeles
June, 1964

CONTENTS

CONTENTS

PREFACE

I. M. Sechenov's *Autobiographical Notes* are most valuable material, not only characterizing the life and activity of the father of Russian physiology, but also reflecting an era when the best people of Russia, champions of the creation and flourishing of science, champions of the welfare of the Russian people, endured the severe oppression of tsarism. The young generation, becoming acquainted with Sechenov's autobiography, will learn under what conditions, and in what a struggle our Russian science developed.

Doctor Belogolovyy thus characterizes 50 years of the past century: "The heavy time of stagnation, the hostility of the government towards the breeding grounds of higher education . . . —all these conditions, which were notable in the epoch described, did not favor the growth and flourishing of science with us, and gave rise to many somber and unfortunate aspects. . . ." During this period in Petersburg Sechenov was beginning his pedagogical activity and was becoming a great scientist, talented teacher, and brilliant lecturer. Here, for the first time in Russia, he began to give a course in electrophysiology.

I. M. Sechenov considered that the "Russian university should be not only an institution where science is propagated, but also a working scientific center where the idea is advanced that one can teach and learn with success only by working."[1] Beginning with his very first lectures, Sechenov drew the youth to himself, organized laboratory studies, and in such a way developed in the youth skills for independent scientific-research work. This initiated the Russian physiological school.

Sechenov, beginning with the very first years of his activity, trying to penetrate the essence of psychic phenomena, created the remarkable work *Reflexes of the Brain*, in which he brilliantly, with extraordinary skill, elucidated this sphere hidden from science. This book called forth the extraordinary interest of the various strata of intellectual Russian society, but in return it was given a hostile reception by the representatives of the tsarist government. I. M. Sechenov went through many difficult and anxious days before this remarkable work was finally published.

The works of I. M. Sechenov in the field of the nervous system, and his great work, *Reflexes of the Brain*, began the development of studies concerning higher nervous activity, so brilliantly pursued by I. P. Pavlov and his followers.

Prof. O. P. Molchanova
Corresponding member, Academy of Medical Sciences, USSR

---

[1] I. M. Sechenov, Brief sketch of scientific activity of Russian universities in the natural sciences, *Herald of Europe*, No. 11, 1883.

1

CHILDHOOD (1829-1843)

ALEKSEY IVANOVICH SECHENOV, our grandfather, and a nobleman of Kostroma province, although a prosperous landowner, nevertheless taught his children the value of money, and entered his sons in their early youth into the guard regiments, according to the custom prevailing in the time of Catherine. Thus, my father, Mikhail Alekseyevich, the youngest son, was a sergeant in the Preobrazhenskiy Regiment, served during the reign of Catherine, and rose to the rank of captain. In childhood I happened to see a paper (probably a decree concerning father's resignation) with the bold signature "Catherine," which father kissed each time the paper came into his hands. Upon the death of Aleksey Ivanovich, my father inherited a small estate in Kostroma province and considerably more property in Simbirsk province, the Kurmysh district, almost on the border of Nizhegorod province, purchased in former times by the metropolitan Dimitriy Sechenov (probably during his episcopacy in Nizhniy) and passed on by him to the family. My father made his home here, having retired under the comfortable circumstances of a Russian landlord in the time of serfdom; and right here (in the village Teplyy Stan) the whole family of his children came into the world: 5 brothers and 3 sisters; I was the youngest in the family. Father's move from Kostroma province to Simbirsk happened, as far as I remember, for the reason that he was a lover of horses, and the grain-producing, black soil of the Simbirsk estate gave him an opportunity to set up a small stud farm, which would have been impossible on the Kostroma estate. Be that as it may, all his life of many years in the country, he was interested only in the stud farm itself; he did not look after the fields, he avoided crown service, he did not work in the nobility elections, and not even

1

once did he go to Simbirsk for the nobility elections. Very little of personal recollections about my father remains in my memory—only some purely external fragmentary characteristics—because he died when I was 10 years old. I remember him as a gray old man, in his everyday house dress (soft boots, black velveteen trousers and a sweater-like jacket) and in a Hungarian dance on holidays, with his pipe in his teeth (I even remember the mouthpiece of his chibouk); I remember how, every day after morning tea, he went to the stables and with his own hands measured out oats for the horses from the bin by the garnets,[1] and then watched how they took the horses to the watering pond; I remember that still during his life I learned to play billiards and mercilessly beat my father, a very bad player, when he happened to play with me out of boredom.[2] He paid little attention to us children; at least I do not remember a single instance where he caressed me or any of my sisters. But, on the other hand, I also do not remember when he became angry with us or punished someone. Even though he had not had an education, he nevertheless realized its importance, and instilled in us children the idea that we must regard our teachers as our benefactors. The governess in our home was a member of the family enjoying equal rights; at dinner she sat in the place of honor, and she called old father *papenka*.[3] Later on I found out from stories that he was notable for his unselfishness and his great integrity; he did not oppress the peasants; he built huts for those who had lost their possessions in a fire; in case of crop failure he gave out bread; but at the same time he did not scorn using, in addition to the corvée, the established procedure in those localities of taking yearly from the muzhiks a sheep for tax, and from the peasants, a certain quantity of yarn. He lived modestly and extremely cheaply "all on his own," owing to the fact that he kept many domestics of which, besides cooks, grooms, and cattle yard workers, two weavers, two tailors, one shoemaker, a stoveman, a barber, a joiner, and even a master of tinware were members. While all the children were still small, he with his frugal mode of life, was wealthy enough that he could build in the village, almost exclusively with his own money, a big, stone church and a two-story, wood house of 20 rooms, with a small garden along the back facade.

My sweet, good, and clever mother was a beautiful peasant girl in her youth, although in her blood there was, according to tradition, a touch of Kalmyk blood through her great-grandmother.[4] Before his marriage father sent her

---

[1] A garnets is 3.28 liter. *Translator*

[2] At this time all my older brothers were already away from home, and only my sisters and I remained in the country with our elders.

[3] A term of endearment, a diminutive of father. *Translator*

[4] Of all the brothers I alone came out like mother's dark relatives, and from her I inherited the appearance thanks to which, Mechnikov, returning from a journey along the Nogay steppe, said to me that in these regions what is Tatar is the picture of Ivan Mikhaylovich.

to a Suzdal' women's convent for instruction in reading and writing and feminine fancy-work; therefore, in childhood I remember her as differing in no way from neighboring elderly manor ladies, who treated her with great love because of her sweet, gentle disposition. The usual half of the household was in her hands; but during father's life in the family her voice was very rarely heard. Moreover, she was not affectionate toward the children; therefore, I came to know and love her only at a mature age, when, upon my resignation from military service, I stayed more than half a year at her place in the country. In childhood, more than my father and mother, I loved my sweet "nurse Nasten'ka," whom, in accordance with her age and position in the house, all the domestics called by her full name of Nastas'ya Yakovlevna. She was affectionate toward me, took me walking, saved delicious candies from dinner, took my part in arguments with my sisters, and captivated me probably most of all by stories, at which she was a great hand. When I had gone to bed, because of the stories, I not infrequently moved to her bed; and when it happened that I disturbed her sleep by demanding repetitions of the stories, she—she told me this herself when I was already a retired officer—began the story about how a certain tsar, planning to build an ivory palace, ordered bones to be collected from all the kingdom and placed in water for soaking. With these words she became silent, and when I asked what happened next, I received as an answer: "There is nothing to tell, my dear fellow; the bones are still getting wet; they are not yet soaked," with which, according to her, I was satisfied.

Our family fell into three groups according to the ages of the children. My two oldest brothers and oldest sister (Aleksey, Aleksandr and Anna), who were a year apart, left the family when I was not yet born, and they studied in Yaroslav. My brothers finished the course in Demidov lycée, and my sister in a boarding school. Father, as a military man and a lover of horses, entered my brothers in the hussars, but he brought my sister, when she finished her studies, back home, where she even began to teach the third group, my two youngest sisters (Varvara and Serafima) and myself, reading and writing. At this time the two middle brothers (Rafail and Andrey) were studying away from home, in our district town, and from there entered the Kazan' secondary school. Thus, all my childhood I grew up in the village as the companion of two younger sisters. During father's lifetime there was talk about sending me to the Kazan' secondary school; but with his death, mother for some reason kept me at home until I was 12 (probably counting on preparing me at home, not for the very lowest class); and at this time my oldest brother, a hussar and already an officer, became acquainted in Moscow with a family, a member of which was an engineer, and learning from his stories about the advantages of engineering service and the low cost of the education received at the Main

Engineering College,[5] pressed mother to send me there. Owing to this, I continued to study in the country until I was 14. This circumstance was of great importance for my future—of all the brothers, I alone studied foreign languages in childhood. The fact was that my parents did not consider it necessary to teach boys languages at home, thinking that they would be taught languages in school; but they considered such instruction necessary for the girls. With that end in view, in our home, a year before father's death, for the sake of my sisters, Wilhelmina Konstantinovna Shtrom of Smol'nyy, who knew French and German, appeared; and at the same time they put me, in addition to my sisters, in her hands.

Before the arrival of the governess and for some time after her arrival, I was taught God's law, arithmetic, Russian, and Latin by a young clergyman from the neighboring village of Atyashev, who was notable, however, not so much for his qualifications for the duties of a teacher as for his pleasant appearance, cheerful disposition, and his ability to conduct himself well in a noble society. As far as I can recollect his lessons, his knowledge of arithmetic did not go beyond the limits of the four elementary operations, and in Latin my teacher was not he, but the Latin grammar of Koshanskiy, since my whole task consisted of learning by heart the rules given in it for declension and conjugation according to the instructions of the teacher—"from these to these." On the contrary, Wilhelmina Konstantinovna's teaching of languages went very well, thanks to the fact that the grammar, precisely, was pushed into the background. The class lessons on languages consisted of our learning by heart one verb each day, copying it from the book (of course, after avoir, etre, haben and sein had been done); then we did small translations from the foreign language into Russian and the other way round. In addition, from the very first year she made us speak in the foreign languages both in and outside the class. I remember this by the following incident. From memorizing conjugations I learned that in French the plusque-parfait corresponds to the past tense with time long ago; therefore, I answered Wilhelmina Konstantinovna's question about the meaning of the word "long ago" by the word "plusque," at first to her astonishment, and then, when the matter was cleared up, to her gay laughter. Be that as it may, Wilhelmina Konstantinovna did me a real favor in teaching me both languages so that I did not forget them during my stay at the engineering college (where instruction in languages was unimportant) and could make use of these accomplishments during my time as a student.[6]

[5] At that time the fee for the maintenance of a pupil, including the teaching, for the course of 4 years, consisted of the payment of 285 rubles; the pupil on leaving with an officer's rank received his uniform free of charge, with the exception of a frock coat and overcoat.
[6] The lack of knowledge of languages of the majority of our students represents a great

I probably learned easily because they often let me leave class before my sisters, and never punished me, whereas sister Serafima sat (according to a custom brought by Wilhelmina Konstantinovna from Smol'nyy) wearing a paper with the inscription "for laziness."

I had a great inclination in childhood for reading, but there was nothing in the way of books for children's reading at that time. I remember only Kon'ka-Gorbunka (for some reason, in manuscript), an abridged Robinson with pictures, and a certain illustrated edition of sacred history, which my sister Serafima and I illustrated, painting the faces of the saints with red paint, and the faces of the biblical sinners and villains with green. I cannot help recalling regarding this that sometimes Nasten'ka made drawing brushes for me from her own hair. Later, probably under the influence of one of my older brothers, Aleksandr, the small library of Teplyy Stan was enlarged. He was a great admirer of Marlinskiy, and went, probably for that reason, immediately upon father's death, from the hussars to the Caucasus as a Cossack of the Line and was considered in the family almost as a man of letters because he wrote from the Caucasus in a literary manner. Be that as it may, we acquired some Pushkin, Zhukovskiy, Marlinskiy, Zagoskin and Lazhechnikov. Probably under the influence of conversations in the family, my favorite author was Marlinskiy, and I read him through from cover to cover. I know for certain that I read all the stories of Pushkin, I knew almost by memory one of his tales, and I read *Ruslan* and *Eugene Onegin* (an edition with pictures), but I was not carried away by poems, and probably I preferred *Yuriy Miloslavskiy, The Ice House,* and *The Novices* to Pushkin. I read all of this without the guidance and instructions of a person educated in literature; therefore such things seemed to me the pearls of creation, where the heroes were characters who performed feats of valor. Thus, my childhood favorites were Ammalat-bek, Mulla-Nur (Marlinskiy) and the Dnieper Cossack Kirsha in *Yuriy Miloslavskiy.* However, my taste for such heroes remained with me even at a more mature age, when I became acquainted with Walter Scott and Cooper. We did not have any Gogol' in the country, but I succeeded in hearing his *Dead Souls* shortly after its publication in readings of a great friend of our home, the Kurmysh judge, Pavel Il'ich Skorobogatov. He was famous for his ability to read and apparently loved to read in society. At least, each time he came to our place we prevailed upon him to read something new, and he did this willingly, even bringing with him sometimes the literary news. Thus, in one of his visits he read *Dead Souls.*

As a boy I was very homely, black, mop-headed, and greatly disfigured by

---

evil. Time would put an end to it if the method of language instruction in secondary educational institutions were changed.

smallpox;[7] but I was probably not stupid, very gay, and I possessed the skill of imitating ways of walking and voices,[8] which often amused everybody at home and our friends. There were no boys my age either among the family friends or among the domestics; all my life I grew up among women; therefore, I never had puerile ways, or scorn towards the female sex; and besides I was taught the rules of courtesy. For all these reasons I was liked in the family and enjoyed the good favor of friends, not excluding manor ladies and barins' daughters.

Of our friends, closest to us was the family of Boris Sergeyevich Pazukhin: he, a widower, his two daughters, and his sister, Praskov'ya Sergeyevna, who brought them up in place of their mother. He was, as far as I know, my father's only friend in that area; he was much younger, but he outlived father by hardly more than a single year. I saw him rarely because he lived with his family 60 versts[9] from us and came to our area once a year, in the beginning of November, for father's name-day, and at that time stayed with his family for some time on his sisters' estate near Teplyy Stan to hunt with borzois in our cheerless steppe regions.[10] At this time he was our guest. I remember him very vaguely, and I know only from stories of relatives that he was a good man out of the common run, almost the most educated of the Kurmysh landowners, he did not keep either domestics or court lace-makers or embroideresses, he did not make use of either extortion with his subjects or the punitive prerogatives of a landlord's authority. They say that he so won me over with kindness that I willingly put on my entire art of imitation before him, and he laughed a lot when I mimicked the walk and speech of his brother, Aleksandr Sergeyevich. Upon his death, Praskov'ya Sergeyevna moved with both her nieces to a permanent residence on her estate, two versts from Teplyy Stan, and meetings of both families became very frequent. The younger niece, Katya, was the very image of her father—ardent, gay, sincere, a little given to mocking, but very good and loyal in friendship, like her father. To the end of her life she remained the closest friend of our family. She was older

[7] My parents probably did not succeed in vaccinating me against smallpox; I was sick with it in my first year, and it disfigured me alone of all the family.

[8] These ways of walking and voices which I learned by heart in early childhood have remained with me up to now, to 75. I could reproduce them even now.

[9] About 40 miles. *Translator*

[10] However poor Russia is in picturesque views, the country where I spent my childhood belongs, I think, to the least picturesque. The land is black almost like coal, broken into gently sloping ravines, without a single sapling or streamlet for versts, with the sole adornment of sparse groves visible on the horizon in the form of dark quadrangles. This part of the Kurmysh district is thickly populated by Tatars and Mordvinians. The parish of our church was the Mordvinian village Mamleika, and in those times I had occasion to see the Mordvinians in church in their national costumes: a long white shirt faced on the front with red lace; a fringed belt under the belly; a necklace of white cockle-shells, and a very misshapen hat appearing like a forward slanting half cylinder and with perforated silver five-kopek coins hanging from its base. Now the local Mordvinians have merged with the Russians beyond recognition.

than I by 4 years, in appearance already entirely a grown barin's daughter, with a sweet and lively face. She treated me very affectionately, perhaps bearing in mind her father; she was, besides, the only barin's daughter whom I saw often, and I lost my heart to her. Probably I realized, however, that my passion would seem amusing both to its object and to the people around; therefore I succeeded in hiding it even from my sisters right up to my departure from the country to Petersburg. Otherwise, of course, I would have been mocked by my sister Varen'ka, who loved to tease me in general and to bring up the subject of my looks. How strong this feeling was, I do not remember, I also do not remember any particular episodes of this love, I do not even remember thoroughly the face and figure of Katya, but I feel even at the present moment that if she were alive, she would be for me one of the dearest creatures in the world, dearer than the second object of my no longer childish love.

I also cannot but speak well of the Filatov family, some of the members of which I had occasion to meet as friends all my life, until recently.

One half of the village Teplyy Stan belonged to my father, and the other half to Mikhail Federovich, richer than he, older in years, and father of the Filatov family. His younger son, Nikolay, was older than I by a year in all, and we could have been childhood companions in the close neighborhood; but our elders were probably unfriendly, and while my father was alive, our families did not keep up an acquaintance with each other; and in the years after his death, Nikolay Filatov was no longer in the village—he studied somewhere away from home, and we met as companions in the engineering college. Old Filatov was a gardener and a beekeeper; he was not at all occupied with agriculture; all spring and summer he lived in the garden and apiary (in fall and winter the whole family moved to their Penza province estate) ; he never visited anywhere; he never went to church, in spite of the extraordinary piety of the female half of the family; and whether for this reason, or because the bailiff of the manor serfs who managed the estate was stern with subordinates, his peasants did not like him and sometimes considered him almost a sorcerer, because in the cholera of 1848 (I know this from my relatives) rumors went among the people that old Filatov had cast it over Teplyy Stan: they saw him as an apparition before it, as he waved the disease over the village with his hands. I became acquainted with him when I was already a retired officer, when he from old age had already begun to pass into dotage, and probably had begun to confuse the imaginary with reality, because, remaining an intelligent man, he related incredible stories seriously. For example, he assured a neighbor who was interested in his bees that once he had gathered such a huge swarm that, having become established in the birdcherry tree standing in front of the garden balcony, it bent its branches to the ground. He was justly proud of his garden—the garden was really marvelous; but the tender spot in this garden was a small, almost rushy pool, in which one could find many carp and frogs, and, according to his words, sazins of almost an arshin[11] were formerly found. On the drawing-room walls hung two or three old pictures darkened by time, and to the curious it was reported that it was the work of his hands, when everyone knew for certain that he had never gone in for painting. Finding out that I intended to study medicine, he told me that he himself was in the French and German department (his own words) and took it into his head to study medicine; but he could not stand the sight of corpses, for which he was as if put under detention, since the authority thought that he was pretending. Apart from these oddities, this was a very intelligent old man, reasoning very sanely about current events and persons, treating the authorities not without irony, and at the same time a very affable and obliging host with the ladies. Much later I got to know and very much liked one of his sons, Petr Mikhaylovich, an extremely intelligent person, from whom there could have come much good if the country had not engulfed him. At the present time I very much like and respect his daughter, Natal'ya Mikhaylovna, still living, who was in the old days ardent and selfless, who brought up her nephew, Nil Fedorovich Filatov, one of the best professors of Moscow University, who died, unfortunately, so early. I was close, finally, to the family of one of his grandsons, Nikolay Aleksandrovich Krylov, whom I will mention much later.

Evil always lives in the world side by side with good, and side by side with the good people described, 7 versts[12] from Teplyy Stan lived a childless, widowed, old woman, A. P. P., who was in her youth, according to her own words, a great asp. In my childhood she was, however, in a period of atonement for her sins, and I clearly remember with what scalding tears she prayed on Sundays in our church, where she was a parishioner. Tradition says that, grieving over her sins and her incorrigibility, she tried nearly to destroy herself, but chose, as it turned out, not an entirely suitable means. Thinking that man lives on bread, and that without bread each food in general is unhealthy, especially fat, she took it into her head to starve herself on food without bread, but she did not starve, but put on weight, and seeing in this God's punishments for the sin of the intended suicide, she was resigned and began to atone for her sins by prayer and good deeds. With that end in mind, she first of all brought up the daughter of a priest who was somehow related to her, gave her in marriage to Pavel Il'yich Skorobogatov, and upon her death, she brought up the three sons from this marriage. Thus atoning for the sins of her youth, she did not however consider it a sin to rule all those under her with an iron

---

[11] 28 inches. *Translator*
[12] A little less than 5 miles. *Translator*

hand, especially the hay girls. The housekeeper, Katerina Petrovna Bartkevich, was her overseer for them, armed for the purpose with a lash, not a wicked woman in essence, but strictly seeing through the orders which were established by her benefactor in the maids' room. And the following rule was regarded as among such orders: as soon as they noticed that any girl who was not married gave promise of being a mother, they cut her hair, dressed her in white hemp rags and banished her to the cattle yard. Also there was no clemency for the other half, since the village and the district police officer were near at hand. How such a relation to subordinates and true contrition over sins could live together in one and the same person is difficult to understand in our times; but in those times such a combination did not surprise anyone—they considered Aleksandra Petrovna despotic, sometimes to the point of being a petty tyrant, but at the same time a true Christian.[13] Our old men became friends with her; she was even godmother to my older sister, and in my childhood she dined at our place almost every Sunday, having stood on her feet as long as Mass lasted in our church.

I do not know for what reason the eldest daughter of her relative, the Ardatov landowner V. G. E., a girl a year or two younger than I, lived in her house and was considered her ward. The three Skorobogatov sons God sent Aleksandra Petrovna were humble persons, who were meekly carried away by her autocratic whims; but in the girl she found a potion such as she herself probably was not in her youth. It is known for sure that this girl at the age of 10 amused herself by twisting turkeys' heads. The housekeeper, Bartkevich, suffered most of all from her mischief and information about her exploits came from this person; and even the old woman had much to endure from her. The old woman wearied out of all patience, the meek, submissive Skorobogatovs with her admonitions, demands and reproofs; but in the end, she was subdued before the girl, considering her a test granted to her. This interesting person played tricks, according to the story of Aleksandra Petrovna herself, to the end of their life together; when she was already a grown woman, before she was to go to the altar, they began to dress her in her wedding dress—and suddenly she declared, to the horror of Aleksandra Petrovna, who had arranged this wedding, that she did not want to marry the old woman's fiancé, although she had given him her consent without any coercion. Of course, there were entreaties, supplications and tears on the part of the old woman. She yielded, entered the church, the ceremony began, and when the priest approached her with the question, did she take her husband freely, the bride, not answering

---

[13] I cannot help recalling as regards this, my first cousin, Anna Dmitriyevna Tukhachevskaya, whom I visted from time to time in Moscow in the '50's, while I was a student. She was elderly and so devout a lady that she lived in Nikitskiy monastery, renting an apartment there. She was absolutely convinced that we, the gentry, came from Japheth, and the peasants from Ham.

the priest, turned her head in the direction of the old woman and looked at her with a challenging smile. The latter went cold until the bride had answered, "yes." There were similar rumors also about her relations to her husband, but I am afraid to repeat these unverified stories, although there are enough grounds to give credence to them. She inherited her mischievousness from her papa, who led a wild life, made friends with Tatars and gypsies, was suspected of horse-stealing, and was excluded by the gentry of the Ardatov district from their midst. And even on the side of her own grandmother through her mother (not Aleksandra Petrovna, but St. F. B.) she was of unimportant blood. This grandmother sold the families of her subjects separately and, they say, took the girls for sale at the Nizhniy fair.

There was finally, 30 versts[14] from us a certain person (F. G. Z.) who drove her subjects to where they choked her to death.

Yes, this was a time when the contemporaries of Karatayev had gone out of fashion in our out-of-the-way places.

I will end my childhood recollections with a description of the following episode, to which I was an eye witness. In the fall, during threshing, a barley grain got into the ear of one of our peasants, Petr Buzin, and stuck in the ear passage, probably across it, so deeply that after vain efforts at home, he turned for help to the Kurmysh district doctor, Nikolay Vasil'yevich Dobrokhotov, who happened to come to our place just at this time. The doctor did not have his kit with him, and by his instructions our tinsmith bent for him a pair of tweezers with flattened ends from stove wire. However hard the doctor tried to take out the grain with that sort of instrument, he of course could not, and he thought up the following: he rolled up a cotton ribbon into a tube, put one end into the patients's ear, and he lit the other end.

I let the reader judge how much surgical aid had flourished in those times in our district; but I cannot help adding that poor Boris Sergeyevich Pazukhin had to die without it in terrible tortures from a stone in the bladder.

In 1843 my oldest brother was in the Obraztsov regiment in Pavlovsk and probably had settled with mother in advance by letter that he had found a military engineer who would undertake to prepare me in half a year for entrance in the engineering college for 1800 rubles in currency. Therefore, in the beginning of '43 I was sent to Petersburg together with our governess, Wilhelmina Konstantinovna—she to her mother, and I to Captain Kostomarov for a half year of an inexpressibly monotonous, boring, dull life. The matter was that my tutor had no students except me; he was not an effusive man— during the whole time of my studies I did not hear from him either a single affectionate word or a single reproof—and the greater part of the day he was away from home and left me in the company of a striker and his wife for a

[14] 20 miles. *Translator*

hopeless period of sitting either in the small room allotted to me for residence, or in the salon of the striker—the kitchen, since with his departure the captain locked all the rooms except these two and the corridor which joined them. It is difficult to believe that in the course of an entire half year (excluding Sundays and holidays) I went out into the street only once a week, in the evening, to the neighboring bath house; and only one time did he himself take me on Nevskiy to the Dominik and treated me there to a spread. Our day began with tea in the dining-room, at which we both sat for the most part in silence; then in the course of an hour he gave me a lesson in arithmetic, which I really understood from him. After this he left for his service, and at noon they fed me lunch, where very often the rather bad cheese of Meshcherskiy played an important role—probably this firm had just then begun its activity and could not make it better. . . . At 3 o'clock I sat down with him to dinner—the cooking of the striker's wife. What the dinners were like, I do not remember; but I got the impression from them that my patron constantly suffered from lack of appetite, because he hardly touched his food. After dinner he moved off into his study, where I was not admitted even once, and at about 5 he came out to evening tea, served to us as supper. At 9 o'clock the bed was pulled out from the bed-closet standing in my room, and what happened then in the house, I do not know. One thing is certain, the captain did not have guests either in the afternoon or in the evening, and an imperturbable silence always surrounded me when I lay in bed. Two or three times a week there came, supposedly to teach me Russian and French (German probably was not required for entrance in the college), a young second lieutenant, a shipbuilding engineer, with a disgusting French pronunciation. The instruction was concluded by his dictating from a book and correcting my mistakes, and from time to time he gave me verses to learn by heart. From his lessons there is left in my memory only: all of *The Miller* of Pushkin, a fragment from *Yermak* of Ryleyev:

> They entered into battle face to face,
> Chest to chest, hand to hand,
> The oak-groves wail from their cry,
> Their feet dig in the ground.
> . . . .
> . . . .
> Now this one, now that one is turned aside,
> They whirl . . . and Yermak has conquered,
> Now you are mine, he cried,
> And henceforth, all is subject to me.

and a fragment from Pushkin's translation of Mitskevich's verses *Three Sons of Budrys'*:

> There is not a tsarina on the face of the earth
> More beautiful than the Polish girl:
> She is gay—like a kitten at the stove,
> And red as a rose,
> And white as cream,
> Her eyes shine like two candles.

The study of grammar, history and geography, by the textbooks accepted at that time for entering the college, was left to my own discretion, with which aim these textbooks were always to be found in my room. However, they did not ask me whether I made use of them.

No less strange was the entrance examination in the college. It took place in the beginning of August and lasted, it seems, one day in all. I remember clearly that for me personally the examination consisted of the solution of problems (beside me sat a boy who wanted me to help him) and in written responses in Russian and French, their having asked me whether I could speak French. I had no examination in history and geography. It is possible that privileges were made about the examination for the post-graduate students who had prepared for entrance in the preparatory boarding schools kept by engineers which existed at that time;[15] but it is also possible that importance was not attached to accomplishments in history and geography because they taught us geography in the college two years and history three.

It is remarkable that in my heart there were no hostile feelings towards Captain Kostomarov—during my life at his place I did not complain either to my brother or to my former governess, whose family I visited on Sundays and holidays not only this half-year, but all the time of my stay at the engineering college, since I had no other friends except this family in Petersburg. Not knowing city ways and not having lived before among strangers, I must have thought that there could not even be a different form of existence in a strange land.

The family of Wilhelmina Konstantinovna included her younger sister Olimpiada, already a grown woman, and her most delightful little old mother, Emiliya Adol'fovna, a German from Frankfort on the Oder, who spoke poorly even in Russian, and lived on the small pension of her deceased husband (an Estlander or Liflander,[16] a captain in the Russian service) and a private pension from Count Adlerberg, a court minister. There is no doubt that mother paid them also for me because they took me to the theater, gave me money for

---

[15] Besides Kostomarov's, boarding schools were kept by two more officers, who served in the engineering institute, Skalon and Kleigels (it seems, the father of the later famous Petersburg town governor, who was notable for his particular zeal for order and for having equipped the police for this purpose without the liberty of command, with Cossack whips, for which he was probably honored with the Kiev governor-generalship).

[16] Regions in the Baltic states. *Translator*

cabs and later, when I learned to smoke, for tobacco.[17] The year after father's death Emiliya Adol'fovna came to our place in the country to see her daughter; consequently, I had been acquainted with the two older members of the family for a long time and, due to their extreme kindness, I felt at home in this sweet family. On holidays and Sundays, besides myself, two cadets of the second corps, the Mikhaylovskiy brothers, visited them. The older of these, Nikolay Andreyevich, the future husband of my eldest sister, had just graduated, and studied so well that he came out an officer in the guards, in the Finnish Regiment. While he was still a cadet, he was greatly interested in literature—in their corps, by his words, there was an excellent teacher of literature; therefore, on holidays and Sundays in the Shtrom family's little drawing room there were very often readings aloud and conversations in connection with what was read. Here I became acquainted with Russian literature much more than at the engineering college, where old Plaksin, who did not acknowledge Gogol' and placed above all Derzhavin and Krylov, was the teacher of literature. The ode *God* he considered "the aquiline soaring of a genius to inaccessible heights"; the beginning stanzas of the ode *Waterfall* were not attainable for anyone in their perfection in the matter of description of nature's beauties; and the words "Word of times, peal of metal," etc., made him tremble, and he recited this ode in a kind of a toneless, sepulchral, voice. And when it was Krylov's turn, he was changed now into a sweet-sounding nightingale (*The Donkey and the Nightingale*), now into a cunning, flattering fox (*The Fox and the Crow*). These were two other pearls of Russian genius. For the unpretentious Shtrom family, not having any friends except us three boys, Sundays and holidays were obviously festive days. Emiliya Adolfovna herself set off then for the Hay Market with a bag of provisions, cooked them herself, and her delicious dinners, soup with quenelles, pie with sig and roasted hazelgrouse, be it said not in reproach to the Kostomarov's dinners, I have not forgotten, and remember till now with great pleasure.

[17] Until I left the school as an officer I never had any pocket money.

2

AT THE ENGINEERING
COLLEGE (1843-1848)

FOUR CLASSES of younger pupils, called *guides,* and two officer classes made up the school of military engineers, under the name of the Main Engineering College. Guides' studies continued 4 years, and then the pupils were promoted to officers, with passage into the lower officer class. Of the guides there was customarily a staff of 125 persons in all, and they formed the so-called *guide company,* with the company commander (a colonel) at the head and his 5 or 6 assistants (usually field-engineer officers) in the role of supervisors (not teachers, as in the cadet corps of those days), taking turns on duty. Upon entrance into the college (at not less than 14 years of age), we immediately took an oath and were considered junkers by law, being in state service; therefore we were spared from the corporal punishment then practiced in the cadet corps. But apart from this, the whole external military regime was the same as in the corps: for the first two years the pupils were considered privates; in the third year they rewarded those who had distinguished themselves by their conduct and by front-line successes with the rank of private first-class, with the corresponding stripe on the shoulder-piece; and in the older class the most deserving of all was made a sergeant-major; after him in descending order of merit two or three were promoted to senior, and a larger number to junior, non-commissioned officers. The job of sergeant-major, when the pupils formed in a column to go to breakfast, to dinner or to class, consisted of remaining alone outside the formation and commanding the column to go left or right. Besides this, every day in the morning he went to the quarters of the company commander to report that everything was satisfactory in the company. At this time he, of course, could have reported a great deal else; but during my time our commander, Baron Rozen, was such an honest man that he hardly would have tolerated the information of a comrade against comrades. At least for the whole time of my stay at the college nothing of the sort came to light. The job of the non-commissioned officers was still easier—they took turns on duty in the company and had only to get up earlier in the morning than the others, to wake the lazy ones for rising. However, this was a problem not entirely easy—in youth one sleeps, as is generally known, very soundly, and we had to get up by the drum at 5:30 in the morning because breakfast[1] was finished at 7, after which we went immediately to our classes.

The inspector (a colonel) managed the academic part for both the officer and guide classes; and above all stood, in the rank of general, the head of the Main Engineering College (in the first year of my stay—General Sharngorst).

Our college was housed (and is probably housed also now) in the main part of Emperor Paul's former palace (therefore called the engineer's castle), along the front facing the Summer Garden. The bedrooms of the guide company (5 rooms), office, storeroom, recreation hall and quarters of the company commander, occupied the lower floor; and the 4 rooms of guide classes, the model room (over the recreation hall of the lower floor) and the two rooms of officer classes were on the upper floor. The location was, of course, splendid, the rooms were high and light. To the gladness of the smokers, in the stoves of the very tall building there were such strong drafts that smoking over the dampers did not leave any traces behind. Smoking was forbidden, but was not strictly prosecuted; one had only not to get caught on the spot of the offense (and for this, of course, measures were taken, in the form of guard duty) and not smoke up the room. There were no gymnastics, but there was somewhere to run in free hours: from the recreation hall there was an exit onto the rather large parade ground (along the whole front facing the Summer Garden), where they permitted us to go in all seasons. In the time of Nikolay they accustomed servicemen to cold: the sole warm dress even at 25° below freezing consisted of overcoats not lined with anything, of dark blue cloth (considerably thinner than soldiers'), which were then worn sleeved (and in warm weather were carried in a cape), earflaps for the ears and mittens, stiff and

[1] They fed us rather well in general, especially on Tuesday, when after dinner there was fairly good pie with jam, a gift to the engineering college from the personal means of the grand prince Mikhail Pavlovich; but after supper they gave us burda, which I could not drink the whole 4 years—watery barley coffee, boiled with milk and treacle.

white as chalk, on our hands. We paraded in our overcoats only upon leaving the college; in the building itself, and in winter during performance on the parade-ground our attire consisted of trousers of a gray-bluish color and jackets with shoulder pieces and stand-up collars.

At the college there was a church and its own priest, Rozanov, with a master's cross; I remember that in the evenings he sometimes came to our sleeping quarters for religious interviews, which, however, were not compulsory for anyone; but whether he taught us God's word, I do not remember, although I cannot maintain the contrary. If he taught it, then it was in the lower class, and one year in all. Classes were numbered from bottom to top; fourth, third, second and first. Mathematics was taught rather well. In the lower class there was arithmetic; in the following—algebra, geometry and trigonometry (they did not teach spherical) ; in the second class analytic geometry (without higher analysis) and descriptive, including perspective, theory of shadow and theory of arches; in the senior class differential calculus (the teacher was lieutenant Pauker, who was later for a very short time minister of ways of communication) ; in the lower officer class integral calculus (the teacher was Ostrogradskiy)[2] and analytical mechanics (the teacher was the builder of the Nikolay bridge, Colonel Kerbedz of ways of communication). It is still worthwhile to speak well of the lessons on the history of architecture, which seemed to me very fine, a fine statement of new history by the teacher Shakeyev, and the history of French literature in the senior class by the very good teacher Cournand. The teaching of the principal subject—fortification—lasted all 6 years, beginning with a description of the art of binding gabions and fascines; but my heart did not lie in engineering work, with all its accessories, drawings of different kinds—physics was my favorite subject in the senior class; and proof that I studied it with success was the circumstance that at the public final examination, which took place in the presence of Gerua, the head of the engineers, and many other generals, the teacher of physics chose me for the answer in his own subject. I remember that just before this he had received from Germany the electromagnetic mechanism of Stehrer, taught me how to use it in his apartment, and at the examination I produced all its operations. Each of us knew in advance what he would answer, but in appearance the examination took place by cards which lay on the table before the head of the engineers, and the examinee, after a low bow to the important person, took a card from the small group, before his eyes. In the lower officer class my love

---

[2] That year when I heard him, he lectured very little; the time was spent for the most part in the solution of problems and in conversations about the campaigns of Julius Caesar, Hannibal and Napoleon. He valued us as mathematicians, for fun, very low; by his words the first mathematician was God, then the great Euler; he put to him the highest number—12, to himself—9, to Pauker—6, and to all of us—zero (he spoke with a Ukrainian accent).

passed to chemistry (only inorganic was given), which Il'yenkov gave. His examination in chemistry I also remember. Mathematics came easy for me, and since I went from the engineering college straight into the university in the physico-mathematical department, a rather good physicist could have emerged from me, but fate, as we shall see, decided otherwise.

The order of the day was the following. From 7 to 8 in the morning preparatory class without an instructor; from 8 until 12—lessons; from 12 until 2—recreation. Those who had money could buy at their own expense (in the dining room of the attendant Galkin) rolls with butter and green cheese and sweet pastries; and for the poor a big basket with rounds of black bread was put out. Many of us poor, in the winter, when the stoves were burning, turned these rounds into dried crusts. The stove chimneys served as drying rooms, and towards evening the delicacy was already ready to crunch on the teeth. At 2 o'clock—dinner, with the singing of prayers at the beginning and end; from 3 to 6 in the afternoon again there were classes. Thus, every day there were 7 hours of studies, with the exception of Friday, when afternoon lessons continued only until 4:30, since in the following $1\frac{1}{2}$ hours company exercise was carried out, that is, marching, various formations on signals and manual of the rifle (guns in my time were still flintlocks). In the evening, before supper, our occupations were diverse: on Monday—fencing for those who wished; Tuesday—compulsory dancing for all; Wednesday—the bath house; Thursday and Friday—the whole evening free; and on Saturday at 6 o'clock —leave for home until 9 o'clock Sunday evening. We had supper at 8 o'clock, and at 9 we went to bed. Whoever wanted to study after supper was given a tallow candle and could study in the washroom even all night. Whoever preferred to study early in the morning would lay a number of pieces of paper on the little table by the side of his bed, corresponding to the hour when the attendant on duty could wake him. There were even tables with two pieces of paper, but I was not among such toilers.

I do not remember the details of my first acquaintance with my comrades upon entrance in the college. I know only that they nicknamed me "thrush" and teased me with the words "chez le capitaine Kostomaroff,"[3] but they did not offend me, although in the college there were those fond of teasing new boys, and there was even the outrageous custom of punishing them for their faults (for the most part, of course, ungrounded and imaginary) with a lash, against which even the authorities for some reason did not protest, although they could not have helped knowing about this wickedness. In my time Stratanovich and Markelov were the artists at this whip of reprisal—I give

---

[3] Probably at the entrance examination, wishing to test whether I spoke French they asked me with whom I studied, and received the corresponding answer, overheard by someone among the other comrades taking the examination.

their names on purpose. I thank God, that he saved me from the hands of these savages, and in spite of my family name,[4] in all my life I have not been whipped. From the events of the first year most of all in my memory have remained: the disease parotitis (mumps), individual training for the front, and the riot against the authorities. I remember this illness because of the method of treatment of it by the college doctor—old Volkenstein. First he cleaned me out with an emetic, and then he gave me such a dose of laxative that I fainted in the infirmary toilet, which roused the attendant nearby, who had probably heard the noise of my fall. I do not know whether I was obliged to this empirical treatment for the favorable outcome of the illness, but the swelling settled without passage into suppuration. The honored non-commissioned officers of the guard field-engineer battalion trained the new boys for the front. The first steps in this study consisted of instruction in the skill of standing "at attention" and "at ease"; then the skill of smoothly raising now the right, then the left foot for marching with light steps. Many years later, when I was studying to be a physician in Berlin, I often passed by Karlstrasse (Botkin lodged on this street) past the barracks, with the parade-ground in front of them facing the street. On this parade ground they taught the recruits standing and marching exactly like us at the college. Just as all military exercises in general are carried out with short breaks for rest, our field engineers from time to time gave us "at ease"; and in one such period the teacher of our detachment, Kuzmin, recounted to us in a lecture how they themselves were taught front-line strategy at Tsarskoe Selo by the present emperor, Nikolay Pavlovich, then a grand prince. He stripped them naked in the arena to see their actual bearing and demanded that the authority not to let the soldiers sleep crooked. If the authority noticed one such, he woke him and gave him a rating; a first and a second time he pardoned him, and then—don't be angry.

The riot occurred by the following chance. When we entered the college there remained in the lower class the next year Prince Ye., who was a sensible boy, but was notable for his unconquerable laziness.[5] He was lazy as before even in the second year, and rumors reached us that his parents made a request of our authorities to use a birch rod for his correction, and this was sup-

[4] "Sech'" in Russian means "to whip"; "Sechenov" would thus mean one who has been whipped. *Translator.*
[5] The devices to which he resorted on examinations in mathematics are worthy of description. On all cards which were hard for him he wrote in the smallest handwriting, on separate little papers, the calculations necessary for the question, in the order in which he would have to write them on the board, and hid these answers on his person in the following order: several cards behind his tie, several cards in the spaces between his jacket buttons, and the rest in his pants pockets. Receiving a card from the examiner's table, he knew by its number where to find the answer, and copied it, while standing at the board.

posedly carried out. This illegal action alarmed the older pupils, and it was decided to protest to the main authority, General Sharngorst, in the following form: to respond with general silence to his customary presence at the very first meeting which was to take place, which was punctually carried out. For this, Sergeant-major Zeime was deprived of his rank; they condemned all of us to staying in the college on Sundays and holidays during the course of a year, and soon after this General Sharngorst retired, and Lamnovskiy was appointed in his place. With our venturing of this protest, and with our leader tolerating the institution of whipping in his midst, one should keep in mind that they themselves knew they were dealing in a bad business, and at the least should have abolished this vile act after the protestation, but this did not happen.

Towards the spring of 1844 we new boys, having finished the field engineers' course of study, joined the company formation, and as soon as it was warm, we began the happy time of preparation for the May Day parade. At that time, our studies at home were done out of doors almost every day, and twice there were scheduled repetitions of the parade of the first cadet corps on the parade ground, owing to which we had the great pleasure of passing in formation along Nevskiy to Vasil'yev Island. Here, in addition to all the military-educational institutions, there were gathered sailors, students of the Institute of Ways and Means of Communication, mining students, foresters—all, properly, in military full-dress coats, with guns. General Schlieppenbach made the first review, and Grand Prince Mikhail Pavlovich the second, having the patience to pass on foot along the front of all the institutions and to examine closely our outward appearance. This I remember well by the following incident (I do not remember in what year): passing along our front, he poked his finger at the chest of pupil Popov with the words: "Remove to the rear rank for me this sullen physiognomy." The day of the May Day parade was, of course, even more joyful: to this day I remember the feeling of an enthusiastic endeavor to distinguish myself when our company went past the sovereign. And besides, after the parade they fed us with the parade dinner and dismissed us for home. Even more gay was the march to Peterhof camp. After an early dinner we marched in formation, that is, with knapsacks on our backs, toward the Narva Gates. At 4 o'clock the Emperor came there and reviewed those of us leaving for the camp of the military-educational institutions. In Krasnyy Kabachek there was a halt, where they treated us to tea. They also gave each one a roll with butter and veal. During this halt we, the engineers, spent the night in some Finnish village, slept in huts on straw, and got up very early in the morning so that before our passage to Peterhof we would have the opportunity of riding Finnish ponies (it was good that the masters did not charge us much). During my childhood at home I loved horseback riding with a passion and eagerly rode on the Finnish ponies with inexpressible delight. At the entrance to Peterhof the emperor again met us and reviewed us.

The camp field in Peterhof embodied a vast, completely level area of meadow. A road ran along the front of the camp, upon which there passed rather often, only the members of the imperial family. Beyond this road but parallel to it, ran a so-called line with the emblems of the institutions at which all pupils took turns on duty, and they called all of us out "to the line" as soon as anyone from the tsar's family passed along the camp road. Running out, we formed and answered with a unanimous "We wish you health," even to the young members of the family who were hardly able to greet us. Behind the line were the pupils' tents in two lines, behind them were the tents of the commanders, still farther back were the dining rooms with the appearance of sheds with awnings, and finally the rear parade ground with various services.

The annual camp was composed of institutions in order of their arrangement from right to left: guard sub-ensigns (and cadets in the second line) ;[6] the engineers (and pages in the second line) ; the regiment of nobility, artillerists and three cadet corps (first, second, and Pavlov). Upon its left wing the camp joined the English garden, with a river not wide, but deep, flowing along it.

They spoiled us in the camp. They did not torment us with exercises, so that there was plenty of free time; they fed us better than in town; they often took us to the coast to bathe; on weekdays they let us visit our camp friends (we were friends only with the artillerists), and on Sundays and holidays they let us walk in small parties (under the responsibility of an elder) in the palace garden and even in Aleksandriya, where the tsar's family lived. Every year, on some important royal day, there was the celebrated illumination of the palace gardens; then they led us walking with large groups of officers along the lanes flooded by the lights. During the first year of my camp life in Peterhof the wedding of Grand Princess Ol'ga Nikolayevna was celebrated with great festivities. On one of the strolls during these festivities I remember a pond, on which there were boats adorned with lights, with singers; and lawns studded with multicolored lights. I was sorry for one thing—at the camp there was no library from which the pupils could have taken books for reading, and there was much free time and nowhere to spend it. However, even in the city the matter was little better in this regard: there existed, of course, a college library, but we did not even know where it was located. They dictated our lessons to us, and we were examined on our notes.

I will finish this cursory sketch of camp life with a note having some historical interest. The later famous associate of Aleksandr II, Dmitriy Alekseye-

---

[6] This was an institution for wealthy people, with the privilege, upon finishing the course, of coming out as a Guard—the institution in which Lermontov studied.

vich Milyutin was a minister; during these years he was a lieutenant-colonel on the General Staff and occupied a post at the annual camp of military-educational institutions, because we saw him on our school parade ground when drills for the whole detachment were carried out.

In my youth I had a way of taking the lead in pranks planned by my comrades, and this was probably noticed by the authority during the second year of my stay at the college, because once at a geometry lesson the teacher, Colonel German, a kind old man in essence, who treated us like little children, called me to the board to answer with the words: "And to the board, just perhaps, Mr. Sechenov, ringleader of all the pranks." However, the pranks of that year in which I took part were of so harmless a character that I never sat in the punishment room. I learned rather well (I was in the first ten), and I was successful along the front; therefore, with passage into the second class I received a private first-class stripe on my shoulder-pieces; but in that same year I committed two acts of misbehavior—one foolishly infantile (I had just turned 16), and the other miserable in its outcome, though coming from motives which had appeared to me as good ones.

I do not know why, but the civilian German teachers were not held in respect by the pupils, and especially the teacher in the third class, Miller, who did not know how to behave with dignity and trembled before the authorities. He especially feared the grand prince Mikhail Pavlovich, and once, upon the arrival of the latter in class, we were witnesses of how poor Miller, pale and confused, almost shook from fear. From this arose my first foolish misbehavior. Somehow, once during the hour when Miller was the teacher in the third class, there was no teacher in our second class (the rooms were side by side), and among the 16-year-old smarties arose the idea of scaring Miller. To this end I undertook to portray the grand prince; for some reason they put a mask on my face, with openings for the eyes and nose; they opened the door to the third class with noise and the words "The grand prince is coming," and I entered there, to the loud laughter of my comrades. The officer on duty (Captain Nemytskiy) immediately ran to the noise, tore the mask off me, and took a meek slave off to the punishment room, to be put on bread and water. Our punishment room was abominable—a dark corner shut off from the so-called watch room, without any furniture, and without even a bed. They dressed the prisoner in old, worn trousers and jacket, and gave him only a pillow since he had to sleep on the bare floor. But it was good that under the door there was a crack through which comrades brought edible dole to the prisoner, otherwise sitting in such a place in the course of several days would have been really a cruel punishment. Whether I sat there for a long time I do not remember, but I left there without my private first-class stripes—degraded.

Now about the other deed.

In private institutions, owing to the daily contact with the authorities, the pupils have the opportunity for noticing in their superiors the outstanding traits of character, and can even hear much about them beyond the walls of the institution, in their own family or from acquaintances. From this comes favor toward some and dislike for others. Thus, a general favorite was the kind, playfully-authoritative Colonel Skalon, who came on guard duty in the full-dress coat of the guard field-engineers, with velvet lapels. We did not greet him otherwise than kissing him on the velvet breast. We liked and respected the commander Baron Rozen, in spite of his somewhat severe look and coldness, and we knew that he was an upright honorable man, but we did not take a liking to the new chief superior because of his manner of address and of rumors from without. In addition to this, from the very first year of his entrance, rumors began to circulate among us that he had brought espionage into the college and they even pointed out a pupil who was occupied with this profession. Whether or not this reform was justly attributed to him I do not know, but that espionage existed will be shown further beyond all question. Of course, one could not like such an innovation, and I decided, not saying a word to any of my friends, to write a letter in disguised writing to the general on one of the holidays, in which the impropriety of the institutions was shown, and there was a warning, as I now remember, in the following form: "Look, Your Excellency, after the feast comes the reckoning." However, I was not brave enough to sign my own name to the letter and, sending it off, I prepared myself beforehand for the fact that the author could be discovered, and I meant to repudiate flatly my authorship. Following this, there were no searches among the pupils, and I was silent for a very long time, but finally I could not stand it—I probably considered my brave deed an underhanded exploit— I wanted to share the glory of the exploit with a friend. How it happened that pupil B., with whom I was not especially friendly, turned out to be such a friend, I do not remember, but I know for certain that the secret was revealed only to him, and I know just as certainly that the story of the letter remained unknown to all the rest of my friends right up to my leaving the college (otherwise, in the course of the following 3 years someone of them would have had a long talk with me about the letter, which did not happen). Nevertheless, soon after my talk with B., the officer-supervisor on duty called "Tack" came down upon me by surprise with the words: Now then, such libels you write to the authorities." Long since having prepared for a rebuff for such an assault, I was not put out of countenance, looked at him with puzzled eyes, and answered that I did not indulge in this. Some time later Baron Rozen summoned me to his quarters and said: "What is this you have done, sir, you wrote an abusive letter to the superior." The Baron could not, of course, question me since it was reported to him by the supervisor on command; but I was sure that he was very happy when I calmly repudiated this charge because he did not try me, and immediately let me go. From that time for several months the story disappeared without a trace. At Lent I went to confession to our priest Rozanov and he asked me, among other things, whether I wrote the letter to the superior. "Yes." To the question of what was written in the letter, I gave him everything word by word from memory. After the sacrament they usually gathered us in the recreation hall; the general came and congratulated us on the admission of our secrets. At this time, after the congratulations, he called me up in front—I came up and I thought: I am lost—instead of that, I heard the following words: "For the sake of this day, festive for you, I am forgiving you your fault through which you were deprived of your private first-class title, and I return to you this title." What this was, an absolution for me of my more serious sin, or a cover of the sin by the priest, I cannot say, but I think—rather, the latter; judging by the fact that there was no gentlemanliness about our general, and by his attitude towards me afterwards.

In the senior class I was made a non-commissioned officer (i.e., I received, according to military custom, a kind of rank giving me some power over young pupils) and I again committed an offense before the general. This year for some reason there was a fight between the pupils of the second and third classes and in punishment for this they were deprived of the right of drinking their tea during the evening (after classes) in the dining room. This measure, of course, was kept strictly by the officers on duty, but the son of the supervisor who was in the third class escaped it. From six to seven in the evening he always went to his parents' quarters (which were in the same building) and of course received some refreshments, and continued this habit even after the story, when his comrades were condemned to rounds of black bread in the evenings. To us, the older ones, this circumstance seemed an unjust affair, and I, on behalf of the senior class, forbade pupil Lamnovskiy to go home to his father in the evenings. No direct measures against me followed because of this, but the general, as we shall see, did not forget this incident. I studied rather well and in this top class as a non-commissioned officer I was careful, was not observed in any other faults, and even enjoyed some favor from Baron Rozen. I noticed this by the following incident. On one of my final examinations I was the last to be examined, and the examination lasted several minutes into the beginning of our dinner, so that when I ran down from above, the company was already sitting at dinner in the dining room, and Baron Rozen was there. At my appearance, he met me, as if with some anxiety, with the words: "Well, then, is it all right?"—and receiving a satisfactory answer, he smiled and said: "Thank goodness." He of course knew the general and knew that he was present at all final examinations.

At this year's annual camp our good honest Baron Rozen had to go through two great misfortunes. Old, of a stern campaigner's appearance, he was appointed this year as a commander of the first battalion (guard sub-ensigns, pages, and us), but General Sutgof, the young dandyish and conceited director of the school of sub-ensigns and cadets, commanded the whole detachment. There was no doubt that hostility must have existed between them, even before the incident I mean to describe—for this it was sufficient to look at their figures.

This incident broke out on the front training ground during battalion drill several dozen steps from us. Before the front line, in addition to our commander, stood Sutgof and, as a spectator, Colonel Lishin, who held the same post in the school of sub-ensigns that Baron Rozen held in ours. In some battalions the sub-ensigns made a mess of the constructions, and Baron Rozen, instead of addressing them, said something disapproving to Colonel Lishin about his pupils. From the military point of view this was, of course, a blunder, all the more since the Baron's superior Sutgof was standing near, and at the same time, the commander of the censured sub-ensigns. The general became enraged and shouted with all his might: "What kind of a farce is this, Mr. Colonel, you may leave the parade-ground, away to your tent." The poor old honored colonel, in front of a crowd of boys had to salute and go away from the parade ground on his plain horse.

A still greater misfortune was in prospect for him later.

This year, long before the annual camp, they gave our college, for the first time, pontoons of a small size with other bridge equipment to teach us the assemblage of pontoons[7] and bridge making. We learned the assemblage of pontoons while still in town, but we practiced bridge making in Peterhof on the river, narrow, but deep (we had 8 pontoons in all), which ran along the English garden. After we had succeeded in the last skill, we began to wait for the tsar's review of the pontoon exercise. The misfortune happened at that review; but to understand how it happened, a little digression is necessary.

For front-line exercise they drew us up into three ranks in the following form: in the front they placed those of tall stature who could do well the manual of the rifle, since this rank was in the public eye; they hid the smallest ones in the middle rank; and in the back, the most shut off from the observer, were the worst front-line soldiers among the tall ones. Besides, our guns were not for firing,[8] but only for looks; they were bad ones, and for many occupants

---

[7] Our pontoons had the appearance of oblong boxes like coffins, and consisted in dismantled form of 5 frames, clamps and tarred canvas which covered the box. All of these parts with the other bridge equipment were packed into wagons in a certain order, and there was an exact certain order of actions for the pontooneers in pontoon assemblage operations.

[8] In the military-educational institutions the front-line guns served only for learning the superficial skill of handling arms, and during frontline exercise we only pretended that we loaded the gun and fired. Separate hours were designated for real shooting, outside the front-line exercise: we shot one at a time, one after another, at the objective.

of the back rank, the rusty ramrods were tight to pull out. At front-line exercise, however, this did not constitute an important defect because the possessors of such guns did not have to pull out the ramrods—it was necessary only that the hands of the back row were raised and lowered in time with the hands of the front row in the imaginary loading. But at pontoon exercise the formation was by height: in the front, the biggest, the next after them in the back, and the smallest in the middle. Consequently, many of the usual occupants of the back row found themselves in the front rank.

Thus, one fine day, and an inconvenient one in the highest degree for the college, and besides, not in good time as it should have been, but 3-4 hours before review, an order came that at 6 o'clock in the evening the sovereign would review the pontoon exercises. The day was inconvenient because our Baron Rozen was on that day on leave to Petersburg and returned to camp after everything was finished. We came with wagons to the river, of course with guns, and formed for pontoon exercises. At 6 o'clock the sovereign came alone without his retinue, stood about 25 paces in front of our small group (40 persons in all in a row) and gave out an order: "Manual of the rifle!" Several steps from the tsar, I think even the fellows tempered in front-line tactics would have been afraid, but here before his eyes stood many of those who were used to being hidden in the back rows from the eyes of the mere commander. Sensing a misfortune, Junior Captain S. was afraid, of course, having given us orders in the absence of the colonel. His figure was pitiful, he gave orders in a kind of constrained voice. The manual was done obviously badly because the sovereign frowned still more and more, and finally did not endure it when it came to the method of loading the guns. The ramrod of someone from the front did not come out; the sovereign ran up, tore the gun from his hands, pulled out the ramrod, threw the gun back to him and shouted: "Teach these scoundrels the whole night on the back parade-ground!" The review ended with this. The sovereign left, and they took us to train on the back field. At 8 o'clock our colonel came back to camp, and straight to us; I was sure that the pupils of the engineering college had not during all the years of its existence done the manual of the rifle with such enthusiasm as we did on this memorable evening under the command of our colonel. He constantly praised us, and not for the sake of consolation, but indeed in all fairness. At 10 o'clock in the evening an order came from the palace to discontinue the exercises.

This review did not affect us in any way; but for the fortune of Baron Rozen it remained, perhaps, not without influence. Being in this year (1847) an old, honored colonel with a Vladimir on his neck, he never rose to the rank of general. Upon leaving the college, they say, this stern old man wept and died somewhere in the provinces as a commander of a field-engineer battalion. Peace to the ashes of this honest man.

This year's camps were joyless for the engineers, as the reader sees, but after them a great enjoyment was prepared for us as graduating students in the city: on the day of our return to the city on our beds in the college dormitories lay the officer's uniform ordered before summer with epaulettes (at that time there were not yet officer's shoulder pieces, giving present-day graduating students much less pleasure than the epaulettes.) In my life there have been not a few joyful moments, but there has not been, of course, such a joyful day as this one. You cease to be a pupil, you break out into the open, there are no forbiddances, you live as you please, and even with money in your heretofore empty pocket (on our coming out as officers I, of course, was sent money from home and in addition a collar of beaver fur for my future winter overcoat). One thing grieved me a little—I still had no moustache, but I did not fail to help this sorrow—during the very first days I bought a false one and in the evenings paraded about the streets with it. During the very first days I had a daguerreotype portrait taken of myself in officer's full-dress coat for my mother (there was not yet photographing on paper); and finally, in the first days I so overfed myself on sardines that for a long time I could not look at them. It was well that I did not know to this time the delights of a drinking bout,[9] otherwise I could have run, by qualities of character, to many distressing things and besides, I succeeded in settling so that I did not have to hang about the taverns. In the two outer wings of one and the same house on Shestilavochnaya (later Nadezhdinskaya) five comrades settled, and I was in one of the wings with Postel'nikov and Colonel Germanov. Postel'nikov's parents, according to customs of that time, upon his promotion as an officer sent him an elderly servant who turned out to be a cook. There was a kitchen in our apartment, and this virtuous man undertook to feed the five of us dinner and supper at 7½ rubles per person. For the new ensigns this was important for they received a salary of 300 rubles for the whole year. Living costs at that time must have been inexpensive because with a little support from home I bought a season ticket in September to the Bolshoy Theater for the Italian opera, having heard much of its marvels from comrade Valuyev, whose parents were season ticket holders to the opera from the time of its appearance in Petersburg. I bought a season ticket for a two-ruble seat and received the worst seat in the theater, the last one of the thirteenth row by the side of the entrance door, but I took delight in this seat, probably not less than the lucky people who sat in the dress circle.

It is not worthwhile to describe the everyday life of this year. It was passed

---

[9] When at the college, where I came as a boy from home, I had not been anywhere except the Shtrom family's, where a taste for drinking bouts could not develop. Vodka and wines were not found there. The only spree took place about twice a year on important holidays, in the form of the so-called "mulled wine" with sugar and cinnamon.

in the circle of former friends; it was necessary to study, as before (in officers' classes daily from 9 to 2); new acquaintances were not struck up; there were no cheap entertainment places at that time in Petersburg (once, however, I was in Martsinkevich's dancing school as an observer); so that when the joy of my coming out to freedom settled on my soul, life began to seem even somewhat boring. One delight for me was the Italian opera. In this season sang: two divas, Borzi and Frezzolini, tenors—Guasco and Salvi, bass—Tamburini (I do not remember the names of the others). Here there developed in me a passion for Italian music which has stayed with me until now; and right here delights with the singing of Frezzolini passed little by little to adoration of the diva herself. I did not have thoughts of approaching her—during this year I had already had occasion to make certain that I, with my Tatar physiognomy disfigured by smallpox, was not predestined to make a success with the fair sex—therefore the adoration took place from a distance and did not give me any tortures. But before parting with her, nevertheless I wanted to say to her "farewell" and let her feel that in Petersburg she left a heart burning for her. With this aim during the first days of Shrovetide of 1848 I for some reason considered it necessary to leave home and go to the then well known hotel Balabina on Bolshoy Garden for the writing of a letter to her in French, and I composed it there to the sound of an organ. In the letter she was informed that the author presented to her in farewell, because of the vast enjoyment afforded, the enclosed verses, and would be found at the entrance of the Bolshoy Theater Thursday after the morning performance (this morning they gave Don Juan and she sang Zerlina). These verses belonged, however, not to my own pen, but were written in former times by a teacher of French at Smolnyy, M. Riffé, and were presented upon leaving the institute to Wilhelmina Konstantinovna Shtrom, with whom he was in love, according to her stories. I knew these verses by heart, as I had been her pupil in the country; I did not forget them even at the Engineering College, and I availed myself of them in the present case, and I remembered them even now. Here they are:

Gardez ce voeu du coeur comme un souvenir
D'un ami de votre jeunesse,
Et puisse aux jours de la vieillesse
Votre regard le voir encore avec plaisir.
Ces jours sont loin pour vous,
A pein votre vie est-elle dans son beau printemps
Vous avez devant vous l'avenir et le temps.
Mais la coupe pour moi sera bientot remplie.
Pour moi depuis longtemps se sont évanouis
L'éspoir, l'illusion et surtout le droit de plaire
Vous le possedez au contraire,
Jouissez en. Que vos jours embellis

Par tout ce qui charme l'existence
Ne connaissent ces maux sans espérance
Ces maux par qui nos coeurs sont a jamais flétris.[10]

In these verses I could only change the second line; in place of it I wrote:
Des jours de votre gloire, ma néese[11]

The rest was sent without changes. On the day set I stood at the entrance waiting for her exit for almost an hour. She ran past to her coach very quickly, but nevertheless took a sidelong look in my direction. And this was my farewell to the diva.

I will pass now to my farewell with the engineering college.

The destiny of those who studied in the lower officer class was threefold, depending upon successes in science, demonstrated on examinations: Those who received an average of 47½, with the total mark 48, passed into the higher class as second lieutenants; the second level went without a promotion in rank, and the third left the college with the same rank as army field engineers. I did not study as diligently this year as before, but applied myself to the examinations and had a right to hope for entrance into the higher class as a second lieutenant; but this, owing to the insight of our superior, did not happen.

The principal engineering subjects in the lower officer class were permanent fortification and building skill. For the examination in fortification it was necessary to present a design of permanent fortification work, and they graded us on this; but these drawings could not have had a great significance because there was not supposed to be anything new of our own concoction in them— some one of the well known systems of fortification was traced and colored. Besides this, all who were not experts at drawing and painting (of which I was one) usually ordered these drawings in the engineering drafting department, and this old custom, and the employing of it every year, could not but have been known to the authorities. In addition, Captain Andreyev, who was no less a passionate Italianophile than I, meeting me in the theater at the same performances, regarded me with favor and talked with me quite frequently, not about fortresses and Voban, but about the operas heard and their casts. Be that as it may, he signed the design I had ordered for the examination without questions, not having a presentiment of the surprise awaiting me on the examination in his class (and this examination was first). General Lamnovskiy was

[10] Keep this offering of my heart as a remembrance of a friend of your youth, and in your later days allow yourself to still view it with pleasure. These days are far away for you, your life has hardly entered its prime, you have before you the future and time. But the cup for me will soon be refilled. For me, hope, illusion, and especially the right to please have vanished long ago; you, to the contrary, possess them; enjoy them. May your days be beautified by everything that gives charm to life, and not know these hopeless griefs, these griefs through which our hearts are condemned forever.

[11] Days of your glory, my goddess. [The word néesse was printed in the Russian edition, and translated in a footnote as goddess, as though it were déesse. Translator]

of course present at this important examination, and as soon as I presented the design, he grabbed a pair of compasses and began to collate the dimensions of all parts with the scale added to the drawing (which I did not do). The villainous graphic artist had placed a bridge across a ditch at 5 sagenes instead of 3; this did not escape the general's compasses, and he gave me 15 for the drawing. In other words, he at once deprived me of the possibility of passing to the higher classes as a second lieutenant. Knowing this, I stopped preparing for the examination as one should, and received a second bad mark on my unloved building skill. On my receiving this grade the general did not fail to turn to me with the following words: "If someone had told you before that you would stand by V. and P. (the lowest students in the class) you would not have let yourself go from the farmstead." I swear on my honor that exactly these words were spoken.

After finishing the examinations we all received notices to appear on a definite day and hour at the college. The general came out to us with a list in his hands and announced that he had called us to hear out our wishes and as far as possible to fulfill them. Calling out those who distinguished themselves on the examination in turn, he announced to them about their right to pass to the higher class, asked each one of them if he wished this passage and, receiving affirmative answers, he made notes on his list. I turned out first in the third rank; it was announced to me that I could not pass into the higher class, and to my wish to joint the Caucasus field-engineer battalion I received in reply a short, dry "you cannot." It did not occur to me then that the distribution of us in the third rank in field-engineer battalions was not under his control, and it seemed that the dry negative answer to my application called forth by him himself was only a new display of his wish to take vengeance on me. Therefore, the next morning I put on my full-dress coat and set off for the college to ask the superintendent for an explanation why my wish could not be fulfilled. Fortunately, he did not receive me.

After several days it was announced to me and one of my roommates, Postel'nikov, that we were assigned to Kiev in the second reserve field engineer battalion.

As soon as our orders for post-horses and allowance for traveling expenses were delivered to us, Postel'nikov, I, and the young lad Feofan Vasil'yevich, (a shoemaker by trade) sent to me during the year from the country for service, set off during the height of the Petersburg cholera on our way south.

Could I have thought then that the dishonor of sending me away from the college was fortunate for me? In any case, as an engineer I would have been good for nothing.

3

IN KIEV, FIELD ENGINEER
(1848-1850)

THE BATTALION to which I was assigned, together with the sixth field-engineer battalion, made up the brigade which was encamped in the summer near Kiev, about two versts from town, but in the fall it left for winter quarters. The cadet school remained in town for the winter, as well as those field-engineer officers who were appointed to teach in it. I belonged to the latter; therefore I had to do military service only during two annual camps, and that incomplete since Postel'nikov and I visited his parents on the road to Kiev and arrived at the post at the end of June, several days late. The authorities pardoned us for this fault with an indulgent smile, and we were accommodated very comfortably in the camp barracks (not tents). Besides Postel'nikov and I in the second reserve battalion, Vladykin arrived, in the same year with us, and in the sixth field-engineers—Korev, so that from the very first days we found ourselves in our own company.

Our chief commanders (brigade—General Bukmeier, battalion—Colonel Kekhli) were neither campaigners nor strict masters. I saw the general three or four times during the whole time of my stay as a field engineer. Our colonel, (though, like all family officers) lived outside the camp, appeared before us only for battalion drill, held himself distant from his subordinates and was by all outward appearances a well-bred and honest man: he did not interfere in battalion squabbles, he did not swear at drills, and was irreproachably polite with everyone. One must do justice also to our company commanders: they did not behave overbearingly with us sub-ensigns (in spite of the fact that my company commander M. had the appearance of a "churl" and obviously came from the cadets of the old stock, distinguished by all the classical signs of this type—small stature, solid build, feet awry, and coarse, abrupt speech.[1] And in general the relations between the officers of the "learned army," as the field engineers called themselves, were decent. I consider it my duty to add to this that in both camp posts I was not a witness to either drunkenness or a major quarrel; in general, there was no disgrace among the officers, or even to anyone being hit in the teeth at the front; and only once did I have to be the unwilling witness to the terrible flogging of a poor soldier (Kalugin) from our battalion. They drove him through the formation for the second run after he was degraded from a non-commissioned officer and was considered penalized after the first. All officers were obliged to be present at this barbarian ceremony; our colonel, however, could evade being present, and the commander of the first company, Captain Polzikov, was in command of everything in his place. I saw only how they had tied the hands of the poor man in breeches with naked back, half to a gun, half to a stick, and two soldiers holding the ends of this horizontal support for the wretch led him between two rows of soldiers with long switches. I closed my eyes from the rest, and only after the flogging saw with opened eyes the following scene. The man in charge, Captain Polzikov, noticed among the floggers a soldier who did not strike the wretch with his birch, and as soon as they had taken him away to the hospital, lay the guilty one out before all his comrades and thrashed him 25 times with the birch. This one got up, pulled on his trousers and said: "I most humbly thank you, your excellency."

Our learned army at camp time should have studied most of all field-engineer work, but very little time was devoted to this because apart from the superfluously practiced marching, no other troops stayed near Kiev in the summer except the field-engineers, and we had to fill the guard posts in town. I personally, during these two summers, was occupied about two weeks with a survey in the camp environs and was attached to the chief with mining work where, however, I did not play the role of the doer, but of the observer, since in the college they did not teach us the practice of field-engineer work.[2] No recollections about this activity have remained with me; I remember only that it was greatly to my disliking, that I was a very careless officer, especially after new

[1] It seems to me that the higher authorities were behind us new-comers from the engineering college because in the whole brigade besides the four of us there were only two more from the engineering college—brigade adjutant Tetsner and lieutenant of the sixth battalion Roshe. This was manifested in part by the fact that of the four of us, three from the very first year were appointed teachers in the cadet school, and one its chief-lieutenant —Roshe.

[2] Much later I heard that they began to send the pupils of our college not to cadet camp, as in our times, but to field-engineer camp.

aspirations and goals began to arise in my head, and that I got away with my carelessness thanks to the protection of our brigade adjutant, Lieutenant Tetsner. A school-fellow in the college, he of course knew of my leaving the college, he himself felt burdened by military service, and was my protector. Once he even saved me from an arrest with which I was threatened by the general for careless duty in the battalion.

When we became a little more closely acquainted with our new comrades, there was one among us, in the person of a sixth battalion second lieutenant, Vasiliy Afanas'yevich Chistyakov, who was the most delightful being, woven of gentleness and naïvete, in the form of a carefree eccentric, equally gay in destitution, adversity, and even mortal danger. There was a reliable legend that, starting for the battalion, on leaving the corps, he visited his grandmother along the road not far from Kiev, who presented him in parting with a lambskin coat and a foal. How he brought the latter gift to Kiev, I do not know; but it is known that upon Vasiliy Afanas'yevich's arrival at his post of service he was involved with some new friends in a card game, lost all his money and in addition he gambled away both of his grandmother's gifts. He gave up cards after this, but he had to make good his debts, and in the end poor Vasiliy Afanas'-yevich was compelled to feed on the company cauldron since almost a whole month's salary went for the payment of his debts. We found him in exactly such a position. We became friends quickly, and he became an inseparable comrade of our young circle.[3] During the month Vasiliy Afanas'yevich of course was our guest; but as soon as he received his salary, in return for our entertainment he arranged a party in his hut and we were invited as guests. On the fragments remaining from his salary he entertained us with tea, hors d'oeuvres, and without fail, a bottle of madeira with a small decanter of vodka. He enjoyed himself at these parties so much that he often broke into a dance; he treated himself to everything much more than the guests and only asked that everything be eaten up and drunk. Thus Vasiliy Afanas'yevich lived light-heartedly to the end of the camps (1849), when the following incident occurred. About three weeks before the battalions left for winter quarters, the married lieutenant Roshe invited him and some of our group to his place in the evening for tea. The conversation turned to the charms of married life, and our host, joking of course, turned to Chistyakov with the words: "Why is it, Vasiliy Afanas'yevich, that you don't marry; it's time, you know, and my bride has the right person—my children's teacher, a fine girl, not wealthy, it is true, but you see, for you happiness is not in money." Vasiliy Afanas'yevich obviously took this joke seriously because he became thoughtful and did not answer.

[3] It is necessary to remark that at that time the officers lived in a space which did not form the whole comrades' circle, not unlike, for example, the way the brother-officers live in Germany. In our camp there was not even a room where we could all meet together.

Then during the following week of preparations of the battalions for leaving for winter quarters, when all the officers were free from official work, we, the cadet school's teachers, took leave of Chistyakov (and our other friends) and moved into town. The battalions had hardly left when the news reached one of us that Vasiliy Afanas'yevich had married and he carried all his belongings in a perambulator like a striker. The second half of this news was added, of course, as a joke, but the first was true. Vasiliy Afanas'yevich really had married the bride recommended to him, who probably thought, like the fiancé, that happiness was not in money. In February of the following year I resigned, left Kiev, and heard about Chistyakov only once more, many years later. During the Crimean campaign my former comrade in the college and field-engineer battalion, Vladykin, then already a retired officer, was a traveller in besieged Sevastopol and visited all our forward posts. In one of these in a dugout, he saw a small group of officers, and among them was Vasiliy Afanas'yevich in his usual home-made suit, in trousers and shirt, keeping the bank. By his own words, Vasiliy Afanas'yevich had changed little, and met Vladykin with his usual gay smile.

My first winter in Kiev I became acquainted with two family homes. In one of these, with three young barin's daughters; we cadet school teachers (Vladykin, Korev and I) played the role of young officers intending to entertain the barin's daughters—we played forfeits, even danced once a week on a set day; but in the other home I alone of my comrades was received and the foundations of my fate to come were laid by a young resident of the home.

The field-engineer officer married to their oldest sister took us to the home with the barin's daughters. The head of the family was a prosperous elderly landowner from near Kiev, who lived in town only during the winter in his own home. He was a no fool; he did not like the Kievan monks very well, he knew and related much that was stimulating from their life; he obviously knew the value of education because his eldest son was a student, and he was, finally, a great lover of music. A then well-known Kievan teacher of singing, an Italian (by name, Vaverio, I think), was often a guest in his home, and one evening there was a certain touring pianist-improvisor, Shiff, who was demonstrating his skill. One of the guests would give him a theme, and he would play variations on it. I bring all this in with the aim of showing that the tone in this house was completely decent and that in the eyes of our hosts we by no means appeared as possible fiancé's for their daughters. I will add to this with gratitude that they received us very cordially, and in the spring or fall of 1849 we were even once at their place in the country.

In Kiev, as in a fortress, there was a so-called engineering detachment, and among the young officers of this detachment was Bezradetskiy, in our same year, and two comrades also friends in the college, officers M. and Kh., three years older than us. It is quite natural that as soon as we found out about Bezradetskiy's arrival in Kiev and he found out about our sojourns as field-engineers, mutual visits began. At his place we met both of our old friends, and I soon became intimate with the latter. Probably the story of my leaving the college helped me even here as it had helped me at Tetsner's. Whether much or little time passed after this acquaintance I do not remember, but once engineer Kh. suggested to me that I meet his family; he received, of course, my consent, and took me to his place at Podol. From that time I visited his family once a week during the whole winter of '48 and the first half of the following year. My way along the road took me past the officers' home of the engineering detachment, and I would drop in there for engineer M., and we would set off together for Podol and return together from there.

This was a Russianized Polish family. The father (he was a doctor) and mother were Catholics, and lived in their youth in such an out-of-the-way Russian place that they had to christen the children in the Russian faith. Later he lived for a long time in Kostroma occupied by his private practice, and here a misfortune befell his family. In the time of Emperor Nikolay, Kostroma was one of the exile cities for Poles, and a great fire occurred in it. The governor, not considering it for long, suspected the Poles of the fire and drove them all, without exception, into jail. The doctor's daughter, who told me about the event, at that time a 16-year old girl, found herself among the prisoners. General Suvorov (the later well-known Petersburg governor-general) was sent from Petersburg for an investigation of the affair; the suspicions of the governor were unfounded; everyone was set free, and my narrator even received diamond earrings from Nikolay Pavlovich as consolation for her guiltlessly enduring the stay in prison. Shortly before the time I have described the family moved to Kiev and was leading a very unpretentious life.

In those days when I was at their place with Lieutenant M., the mother never came out to the guests; the eldest son (a communications officer) appeared extremely rarely; the father—an old man—appeared only for a short time; there were never any guests except us two; therefore, our evening company, under the leadership of my young 20-year old benefactress Ol'ga Aleksandrovna, was made up only of her two brothers (the engineer who had brought me to the house, and a younger brother, a university student), and the two of us. The status of a married woman gave her the right to prominence in men's society—she was a widow, having lost her husband a half year after the wedding—and also in spite of her youth, she was by development and very likely also her mind, much above her company. I will not describe her appearance; it is sufficient to say that she was not, like Mitskevich's Polish girl, white as cream and red as a rose; she was not even gay like a kitten at the stove, but belonged undoubtedly to the breed of kittens with agile, lithe stature, and her eyes very often shone actually like two candles, because she was in general of the breed of exultants. Nicest of all about her was her kindly smile, with which she often ended her hearty pranks, when she herself felt that she had run to paradoxes in her enthusiasm.

Ol'ga Aleksandrovna had studied at home, and her teachers were only men (probably from the Kostroma Poles); from here came her taste for serious reading and her serious attitude towards vital questions, with some touch of anger naturally, however, resulting from the general conditions of her exist- ence at that time and the personal ordeals suffered by her. Complaints at the lot of women were a hobby of Ol'ga Aleksandrovna. At that time the book of Leguvé (*La femme*) had just appeared on the Kiev market; she made a great fuss over it, even gave it to us to read, and did not even want to be reconciled to the high role of the woman in the family and the school proposed in the book. She considered woman half jokingly, half seriously, the crown of crea- tion, and I saw in her subordination to a man a great injustice. The course which the Russian woman later took in order to stand on an independent foot- ing was at that time still closed; she admitted the subordinate position of woman with anguish in her heart as hopeless and expected in the future, and in the general progress of enlightenment, only a mollification of her part. It is clear that in the presence of such inclinations, education in man and mental work had in her eyes a great value. No offense meant to us, the military, she placed university education very highly and considered Moscow University as standing above all others—the name Granovskiy I heard first from her. As a favorite hostess she did not touch upon our profession, but she hardly sympa- thized with it—the times were then peaceful for Russia, we were not going to have to defend the fatherland, and the formula "prepare for war if you want peace" was not yet so much in vogue as now. Her thoughts went in the direc- tion of service to her fellow man, and in this sense she regarded the medical profession very sympathetically.

I have purposely written these few extracts from our evening discussions at Podol just because they were deeply fixed in my soul. It is possible that views cited by Ol'ga Aleksandrovna would not have had a great effect on me if they had been expressed in a doctoral tone, with the aim of a lesson. But she did not have the ways of a learned woman, conducted herself on an equal foot- ing with us, and expressed her views casually, lightly, among the habitual general conversations and disputes, preserving only invariably the countenance of a lively, charming, intelligent and educated woman. It is necessary to say that her lessons, beyond their actual value, were deeply fixed in my soul because I lost my heart to her. Under her influence I began to read, I became acquainted with her favorite George Sand, I read Goethe's *Faust* with great enthusiasm, was delighted by Schiller's *William Tell*, and even bought the complete works of Lessing. Nevertheless, I had a little understanding of the leading figures of French literature, but from German literature I knew only the names of writers, and I did not know the English language at all.

I hid my love so carefully that during the whole time of our friendship, I did not encounter on anyone's face, among those present, a single suspicious smile. More correctly, however, my secret was known to all the evening company—her, her brother, and M.—but they looked at me fairly, as at a boy (during this friendship I was 20) who knew how to behave properly, and to whom the first love of youth was beneficial. I concluded this from the fact that Ol'ga Aleksandrovna was always kind to me and meanwhile in her fiancé, M., there were no displays of jealousy: up to her departure from Kiev I continued to go with him every week to Podol, there and back together. I do not know whether I could have been firm if I had known that I was going with her fiancé; but this was hidden from me, and I did not guess it even when, after Ol'ga Aleksandrovna's departure, I found out that M. left Kiev on a 4-month's leave. She left, in her own words, not for long, and saying goodbye to her in Brovary at the first station from Kiev (where I rode to see her off with both of her brothers), I thought that I would not have to feel lonely for long.

Several months passed, in the course of which I lived, obviously, in anticipation of her return because I did not undertake anything in spite of the fact that long ago the idea had risen in my mind to leave the military service. The time passed to Christmas. I was sitting at cards with my friends from the cadet school and I suddenly heard the exclamation of one of them: "and do you know, lady (so and so) married M. and they will be here in a matter of days!" I was taken aback here and gave myself away by an incompatible motion; but they spared me as if they had not noticed and the game continued without further conversation on this subject. After several days the newlyweds really came, and I was at their place for a congratulatory visit. Ol'ga Aleksandrovna seemed to me an entirely different person—an amiable hostess without her former simplicity, and even with another appearance, in a new hair style, a silk dress, and behind a silver samovar. All of these outward changes were of course natural in her new position, and the hostess, of course knowing my past, could not behave so freely as before—she even answered my congratulations a little disconcertedly. But jealousy obviously gnawed at me, the reception seemed to me like a parade, strained, and I left with the decision to be at their place only once more, at farewell.

After this I sent in my resignation.

According to information it turned out that I could take a discharge ticket until receiving a decree about resignation; I did not want to stay in Kiev, but I had very little money in my pocket, and I did not consider I had the right to ask it from home since I had left the service without any talks with my mother. Fortunately one of my friends, Vladykin, was a man of substance, and going home on leave at this time, promised to lend me 200 rubles, and send them to me from his village. An even greater piece of good fortune, our brigade adjutant, Tetsner, finding out about all this, offered me money immediately. He himself intended to leave the military service and regarded my resignation sympathetically. With money in my pocket I got the chance to take off my military uniform and went to say goodbye to Ol'ga Aleksandrovna in civilian clothes. The reception this time was friendly, they sincerely congratulated me for leaving the little-promising service, regarded sympathetically my intention to study, and they wished me every success.

Thus the Kiev episode in my life was finished.

I called Ol'ga Aleksandrovna my benefactress, above, and not for nothing. I went to her house as a youth, to this time swimming inertly in the channel into which fate had thrown me, without a clear consciousness where it might lead me. But I left her house with my life's plan prepared, knowing where to go and what to do. Who, if not her, led me from the situation which could have become a noose for me, showing me the possibility of leaving. To what, if not her influences, was I obliged for going to the university, namely that which she considered foremost—to study medicine and to help my fellow man. It is possible, finally, that some part of her influence even affected my very late service to the interests of women who were struggling for an independent way.

I met with her for several hours after 14 years (1864), when I was already a professor in the medical academy. She came with her hopelessly ill husband to ask the advice of the Petersburg doctors, especially S. P. Botkin. The meeting was friendly, of course, but I did not succeed in expressing to her in a genuine way my gratitude for everything for which I was obliged to her; to recall the true cause of her influence on my fate in the presence of her husband was not easy.

In early February of 1850 I and my dear servant, Feofan Vasil'yevich, started off from Kiev for our own nest, the station Teplyy Stan. On the way there I turned to the Chembarskiy district of Penza Province and stayed about two weeks at Vladykin's, as it had been agreed between us at his departure from Kiev. Here good-natured Vladykin, knowing that during my studies I would be faced with living on the small resources from home, persuaded me to pay off the debt in small portions, and the debt was paid back in three years.

Mother met her retired ensign with tears, but without a single word of reproach. She, according to her words, had always hoped that one of her sons would go into "the learned share," and knowing from my letters that I was

leaving the service so as to go to the university to study, she reconciled herself
with my resignation. The neighbors saw this action otherwise. Old Filatov
lectured to me about his failure in the medical department and concluded his
story as I remember now with the following couplet:

> Professors and doctors
> My soul despises like rabid animals.

Another neighbor, Aleksandr Petrovich P., spoke more directly: "Why,
friend, look at the swell, if he doesn't like the military service, let him have
the civil; our Simbirsk governor will take him, maybe, as an official of special
commissions, since this one of yours is sharp, sensible, and knows languages."
To top it all off, Filatov's youngest son, Nikolay, who had studied together
with me in the engineering college, finished the course in the highest officer
class with honors, joined the guard field-engineers, married the daughter of
"an important civil general" in Petersburg, and intended to come this very
summer with his young wife to the same Teplyy Stan. How could it not hurt
the heart of poor mother! At first she was able to hide from me her chagrin,
but then, probably, she trusted my intention to study seriously, and she was
reassured. Soon we became such friends that she began to confide to me such
intimate sides of her past life as it had been impossible for her to do with
her daughters. Hardly any of her children except me heard her sad story.
And in me she found so sympathetic a listener that almost with fright she
finished one of her narratives with the words: Do not blame (a name), such
were the times then. I must say that I found another friend in my dear
Nasten'ka. Here there was no thought of reproaching me for my resignation;
she was sorry only that she did not have occasion to see her pupil in the dark
blue officer's full-dress coat. She reproached me only once, and even then as
a joke, with a grin, describing how upon Nikolay Filatov's arrival all the
menials went hat in hand to the young man and held out their hands to
them—they were both in arm chairs, he in his dark blue guard coat and she
in parade dress. I found my older sister, as before, bored, behind the tambour,
and became intimate with her only much later in Petersburg; Varen'ka
changed into a slender, cheerful, and mocking young lady; but my younger
sister, Serafima, had already begun to turn into an eccentric woman, which
she later became. During my absence she was a zealous dancer and found
time to be a dashing horsewoman, but she was very afraid of breaking the
girth on a jump and became cowardly. At this time in our home lived two
younger priest's daughters homeless with the death of their brother, a priest
(mother had taken care of them out of love for their brother), and I found
Serafima Mikhaylovna making fun of their training in society manners and
dancing. These three slept on the upper floor in two neighboring rooms over

mother's bedroom, and it often happened that their dancing training took place in the dead of night. Serafima asked mother's forgiveness if the dances had not let her sleep, but she quickly forgot and again began the nighttime diversions. She passionately loved all animals in general, primarily dogs, and this year brought up a wolf cub.[4] Had she fallen into good hands from childhood, something sensible could have come from her.

I could not go to Moscow without a decree about my resignation, and a decree did not come until the beginning of October. I remember till now that the long-wished-for paper came into my hands at the time when I was reading in the book last received of the *Contemporary* Annenkov's letter from the province, where Baryshevskaya settlement was described. I remember also that three days before my departure snow began to fall, a sleigh road was made, and I with my unfailing servant left for Moscow in a sledge. At the town gates it was necessary to show a passport. An old official brought it from the guard house, and giving me back the paper shook his head with the words: "Eh, Mr. Ensign, you served only a few days and you are off to the capital to run through your parents' money."

[4] When the wolf cub grew up they gave him to the landowner Andriyevskiy, who kept him chained in a kennel. More than a year later we happened to go through the village where the wolf was kept. Serafima wished to see him, started off for the kennel, and as soon as she called the penned animal with the accustomed name "Wolfy," the wolf joyfully rushed to her.

4

In Moscow University
(1850-1856)

We stopped at some farmstead, not far from Okhotnyy Ryad and almost immediately set off together to look for an apartment near the university. On Mokhovaya, almost opposite the university, an apple merchant's room in an outwing had been given up, but it turned out to be unsuitable—the master and his servant would have had to live in one room. We went along Nikita and found an apartment in Khlynov alley in the church home of Nikola Khlynov at the church sexton's. The apartment was on the first floor and included two rooms: a half-dark entrance and a kitchen together and a room with two windows, with the windows on the alley. The latter room was divided by a continuous partition, and I settled in one half of it, and Feofan Vasil'yevich in that part of the first room which served as the entrance. He was a shoemaker by trade, but before his arrival in Moscow he had not practiced his skill—in Kiev he had made money by filling cigarettes for officers. And here, soon after our arrival, all the appurtenances of the shoemaker's art were set up in his room, and he sat down to the shoes of the church ladies of Nikola Khlynov. He apparently sewed very cheaply and strongly and could probably do a service to other masters with something because the landlady undertook to cook for us our simple dinner free from our materials. For me this was very important because the following year I had to economize greatly: from the 300 rubles which I received from my mother it was necessary to pay 50 rubles to the university, to pay part of the debt to Vladykin and buy books

(I remember positively that my first year I had the anatomical atlas of Bok and the zoological atlas of Burmeister). I do not know how Feofan Vasil'yevich contrived—concern over our provisions lay with him—but food for both of us during a month rarely came to more than 5 rubles.[1] It is possible that he lived on his own money or even applied it to my food, because relations between us were friendly, and he liked me. All this year I was in a greatly excited mood, I went only to lectures at the university and at home I sat at my books until late in the evening. The only window of my half room opened out on the alley and was so low to the ground that the children acquired the habit of looking in the window at me from the street. This prompted me to cover the lower part of the window with a curtain, and it was not taken down right up to my departure to another room. I remember that this unimportant situation was not in the least a burden to me—I was constantly busy, had had my fill, and the room was warm. Even now many students live far worse.

I do not remember how I found out that one of my cousins, the elderly widow Anna Dmitriyevna Tukhachevskaya (the daughter of Dmitry Alekseyevich Sechenov) lived in Moscow, who introduced me to her, but I do know that I went to her place on Sundays during this year, always found there an elderly gentleman Zverev with his daughter, no longer young, and I always passed the evening in hopeless preference. About another friendship very important for me I will tell below.

When I came to the university office with the question as to what I should do so that I would be accepted as a student in the medical department (in October!); they told me, of course, that now having handed in my request to the rector I could register only as an auditor, but I could be enrolled as a student only the next year upon passing the entrance examination. There was nothing to do, I entered as an auditor with the idea of visiting the lectures of the first year and preparing little by little for the entrance examination. Professor Sevryk lectured at that time on anatomy every day from 8 to 10 in the morning; therefore the first lecture in which I found myself was his. I came and heard to my great chagrin that he lectured in Latin. This of course took me aback because the ability to read Latin remained in my memory only from childhood, the declension of such simple things as *mensa* and perhaps also several verb tenses. Soon, however, my fear was dispelled when I obtained a textbook of anatomy and an atlas, and especially when it came to the lectures on myology because here everything was reduced to a description of the origin

---

[1] My dinner, however, corresponded to this expenditure: twice a week shchi with a piece of beef, on the other days: six soft-boiled eggs, sausage, buckwheat porridge with milk, potatoes with kvas and cucumbers. I drank tea only once every two weeks, after the bath, and in the morning I made kalach from two kinds of flour for 1½ kopeks. From time to time I regaled with bitter-sweet apples, and a taste for this apple has stayed with me to the present.

and insertion of muscles in the following invariably repeating form: such-and-such a muscle *incipitur ab* . . . (a prominence on the bone), *adseritur* . . . (prominence on the other bone).

Be that as it may, I did have to think about studying Latin, and I did not know to what degree it was necessary to study it for the entrance examination and for further university lectures. A friendship with the philology student Dmitriy Vizar helped me out of this difficulty; he taught me how to get down to work. In one of the previous years he was in our area as a tutor in the family, my friend at home, and I found out about his being home before leaving for Moscow; I met him at another student's place—the law student Samoylov, a relative of the people where he studied. They both of course contributed their share to the resigned engineer who wanted to study, and I began to visit them. Dmitriy Vizar's father, an old Frenchman, was a French teacher in the institute at the foundling home, had an apartment at public expense, and lived with his two older sons and two daughters, and his mother kept a small boarding house near the Don monastery and lived in those parts with the youngest son. I was on terms of great friendship with this family all six years of my stay in Moscow, and I was very much obliged for it. One might say that my education, begun in Kiev by Ol'ga Aleksandrovna, was completed in their home. To understand this, it will be sufficient to say that in the family, worship for Granovskiy reigned—at one time Dmitriy Vizar was even his household secretary, and the oldest of the sisters lived some time in the family of Frolov (the translator of Humboldt's "Cosmos"), a close friend of Granovskiy.

The oldest brother, the very kind and noble Vladimir Yakovlevich, was head of the house; upon his father's death his sisters, young girls preparing at home for an examination on the knowledge of the home teacher, were left on his hands. I found him to be an official, serving for tutorial advice after finishing in the university, but without the lowest official mark. He was lively, cheerful, invariably gay, like the true head of a family, he was an unpretentious example for us in all respects; he was very polite with women, but fraternal, without the least allusion to love-making; he apparently lived for the family because outside the home he visited only one old friend, and he cared for his sisters so much that one family friend called him nothing but "Mama." At home in a circle of friends he was really like a sweet, good, cheerful hostess. His sole masculine passion was shooting.

Dmitriy Vizar was an entirely different person. Essentially as good as his brother but without his girlish simplicity and mildness, he belonged to that type of nervous, unbalanced, people who are able to run to extremes—to pass from gloom to fits of mirth, from a serious business to an orgy. An auditor in the philology department, which constituted the pride and joy of Moscow

University, he studied with enthusiasm, became engrossed in reading books,[2] and prepared himself for a learned career. When he was in good spirits he was notable for his great wit, willingly shared the impressions he received from books and lectures—he was, so to speak, a connecting link between the university and his family, bringing to it the spirit of university life. And at that time the university played a very conspicuous enlightening role in Moscow, and Moscow liked it—and not like now, when they are trying to protect the university from the society of bureaucratic regulations with a Chinese wall.

Music was performed in this home by the teacher of the eldest sister,[3] Lady Protopopov, a very good musician who later married A. P. Borodin, chemist and composer of *Igor*. Finally, literature was presented by Appolon Grigor'yevich, who was received at the house.

It is easy to understand that friendship with such a family was a great piece of good fortune for me, especially if one takes into account that medicine at that time, like science, contained very little culture.

I spent the summer of 1851 in Khlynov's alley preparing for the entrance examination. I prospered so much in Latin that I read almost all of Ovid's *Metamorphoses* and asked Vizar for help only now and then. In history I prepared with Lorents' book which was given to me for so short a period that I had to take down excerpts from it. These studies generally took so much time that I had soon accustomed myself to the idea of entering the first year after passing the examination.

Of the minor episodes in the examinations I remember the following. Granovskiy examined me on history; I probably answered indifferently; the examiner was silent the whole time and put down a 4 for me. In Russian we were required to write a composition on the theme "love for parents." I wrote about the significance of the mother for Schiller and Goethe. Buslayev was the examiner. After he had read my composition he asked me whether I had read Goethe and Schiller, and receiving an affirmative answer, he put down 5 for me. Professor Zernov (the father of the present-day anatomist) examined me in mathematics. I remember that I drew a card about the similarities of triangles. At this moment beside Zernov sat Anke, then dean of the medical department, who was so imprudent as to remark: "Why examine Mr. Sechenov, he is an engineer, you know." To this Zernov became angry: "If you want, I will not examine him." Anke of course hurried to correct his mistake, and

---

[2] After finishing university he passed his master's examination and began to prepare his dissertation. Here his passion for reading became the undoing of him: he became engrossed to such an extent that he could not write his dissertation—he began several times and several times destroyed what he had written. He became unsociable, never showed himself anywhere, and in the end put and end to himself.

[3] Leonida Yakovlevna, then a young, beautiful girl, a great friend of mine, who married my friend Vladykin; she studied medicine in Berne then, returning from there as a doctor and taking up medical practice in Moscow.

the conditions of the similarities of triangles were satisfactorily stated. From Latin they made me translate several lines from Sallust.

After the examinations Feofan Vasil'yevich and I moved to a new apartment on Patriarch Pond into a house with a mezzanine with a front facade opening on the pond (by the exit from Malaya Bronnya just to the left, the second house). Our apartment consisted of two rooms and a hall, mine with a window opening out on the pond. When, after a year of life in the half-dark room, set at rest from the examination anxieties, I first opened this window, the Patriarch Pond seemed to me, I think, more beautiful than the Swiss and Italian views which I saw later. I remember that for a long time this window served me as a source of delight, and thanks to it, several persons who every day walked along the paths around the pond are preserved in my memory. I remember, for example, a neighbor about the house, Mr. Kutuzov, a middle-aged man with a military bearing, who always walked with the Khlyst accompanied by a bulldog by the name of "Grishka"; I remember the gypsy women who walked in bright dresses and among them one who was simply a beauty. At that time, however, I was indifferent to the female sex—my mind was occupied by other matters, and I essentially kept on retaining in my heart Kiev reminiscences. They faded only two years after my leaving Kiev, when I was already in the second year.

My third apartment was very original, in one of the lanes off B. Nikitskaya. Its landlord was Prince Golitsyn, who was paralyzed. From his small apartment he let out one room (in which I lived) and a kitchen (in which my servant lived). The prince was in such financial straits that in the shop where he bought the provisions for his table they did not give him anything any more, and he lived solely on tea since the baker had not yet closed his doors to him. Payment for the apartment was of course by the month and in advance. Nevertheless, soon after I settled at his place and paid the proper amount in advance, I received a note from him in French in which the poor prince with profuse apologies asked me to give him 5 rubles on future account. His wish was fulfilled, and I found out that on the next day that he sent to the English club for varenets.[4] A servant woman who lived at the prince's cooked for us like the Khlynov sextant's wife cooked and was by all appearances pleased—everything came her way from time to time, instead of the invariable tea with bread, a piece of beef, milk, eggs and potatoes.

During the year the last part of the debt to Vladykin was paid back, and with passage into my third year I became a wealthy man thanks to the inveterate habit of living economically.

Now I will relate how they taught us in the first two years. Besides anatomy

---

[4] Varenets is boiled fermented milk. *Translator*

and theology, in the first year we were taught several natural sciences: physics, chemistry, botany, zoology and mineralogy.

The anatomy professor, Sevruk, was an anatomist of the old stamp. Lecturing in Latin, he could not, of course, go into a discourse; he not only laid histology (at that time a separate chair for histology did not exist) aside, but he even regarded it skeptically (we heard this more than once in his lectures); therefore, he invariably stayed within the sphere of precise description of the macro-anatomical details of the human body. Within these limits he was a good teacher and—what is very important—he scanned in one year all the branches of anatomy with the same detail (not as is done now); and for this reason those who heard him were prepared for the following year for the studies of anatomical practice in all branches of anatomy.

Having attended a course on anatomy for two years I was so well acquainted with the subject that I thought of getting money by translating Girtle's textbook, and in the summer of 1852 at Teplyy Stan I translated several sheets of this book. On returning to Moscow I asked Professor Sevruk whether I could hope for publication of the book if he would take the translation under his patronage, but the professor refused to patronize it, saying that he lectured according to Bok.

Theology was given by the archpriest Ternovskiy of the university church, of a very pompous appearance, who considered himself a scholar in theology —he wrote a textbook in which the theological theses, taken from the Holy Scripture, were fortified by arguments of reason. At the lectures he sharply watched after the propriety of his own multitudinous auditorium—the first-year students of all departments heard him at one time—and not for nothing: at one of these lectures he told us about the Fall of man's forefathers, and suddenly amidst the general silence was heard "crack." "Mr. Malinin (would this not be the Malinin and Burenin of the physics textbook?), the archpriest broke off his speech—I tell you about an event so banefully reflecting on the fortunes of mankind, and you crack nuts. Have the goodness to leave." The Metropolitan Filaret came to the examination on his subject this year (1852). We probably knew about his coming ahead of time because in the auditorium where the examination took place several strangers were awaiting his entrance, and among them was the historian S. M. Solov'yev, to approach the famous master under blessing. He did not stay long, and I saw only from a distance his small, emaciated figure in a lilac cassock with a white cowl.

Physics (Prof. Spasskiy, the author of *The Climate of Moscow*) was given very elementarily (the complete course in one year) and with a very small number of demonstrations, because the auditorium was not adapted for it— in a big hall (the so-called big auditorium on the second floor with a main entrance), without an amphitheater for an audience, stood a small table on a big platform, and nothing more. We studied with Lents' textbook.

In the same auditorium and behind the same table sat the very kind botany professor Fisher von Valdheim. He lectured inexpressibly boringly, by some old French textbook (I think Richard's), but in contradiction to the arch-priest Ternovskiy he regarded order in the auditorium indifferently. Instead of 100 odd people, not more than ten or fifteen came to his lectures, and the whole year we heard only once from him the admonition: quidquid agas finem respice utbene agis;[5] as well as the stereotyped phrase: "tres faciunt collegium"[6] (which he said, however, with a smile, rubbing his hands as usual, in the beginning of the lecture when the number of listeners had reduced to three). They unmercifully abused his kindness at the examination, answering not the cards drawn, but their own.

The post-graduate Varnek taught us zoology. He lectured simply and clearly, stopping primarily on general indications of levels accepted in zoology, and a description of single-celled animals prefaced a long treatise on cells in general. However, the latter studies fell on unready ground—at that time Moscow had not yet thought of a microscope; therefore Varnek was not successful among the students, and in mockery they even nicknamed him cellule.[7] At that time the enthusiasm was directed to the zoology professor Rull'ye, who loved to philosophize in his lectures and lectured very eloquently.

Mineralogy was given by Shurovskiy without crystallography and in such a form that nothing from his lectures has remained in my memory.

The excellent dissector Ivan Matveyevich Sokolov was in charge of practical studies in the anatomical theater (Sevruk did not drop in on these studies). My two friends in the course, Yunge and Einbrodt, and I worked with him not only in the mornings in the hours set for all, but also in the evenings which was allowed. Ivan Matveyevich himself worked together with us in the evening, making ready the preparation for Sevruk's lecture the next day. He gave himself to his work with great love, finished his preparations with the greatest care, trying to add beauty to them, with which aim he prepared the filled blood vessels to branches hardly visible to the eye and lubricated the muscles with blood. As a dissector of that time he was, in general, in his place. With Sevruk's help (after I had left the University) he was made professor of anatomy and even lectured one or two years on physiology (upon Professor Glebov's departure from the University), but having served for 25 years he was not appointed for a five-year period and remained without work. In this unfortunate position he went to Petersburg to solicit a place, and being without

---

[5] Whatever you do, consider the end, to do well.
[6] Three make up a society.
[7] Much later I learned that Varnek and the well-known botanist Tsenkovskiy were among the first Russian biologists who worked with the microscope during those times.

any connections, turned to Botkin and to me (we were then professors in the medical academy) with a request to help him in finding a position. Poor Ivan Matveyevich added to his request: "Being accustomed to dissecting all my life, I began to scale the wall when I was left without work; from boredom I even began dissecting beetles and cockroaches."

Besides the practical courses on anatomy, the second year they gave us organic chemistry, comparative anatomy, physiology, pharmacology, general pathology, therapeutics, and in this year I think, encyclopedia of medicine.

Professor Ivan Timofeyevich Glebov (who after long service passed on to Petersburg as vice-president of the medical academy), an undoubtedly very intelligent man and a very original lecturer gave comparative anatomy and physiology. One can compare his favorite style of stating facts with the investigator's method of interrogating a defendant. Namely, he did not state the essential problem to which his discourse turned directly, but kept it to himself and approached the answer to it little by little, sometimes even by roundabout ways. Like a clever man, he managed his slow methods of approach and appearance so adroitly that they sometimes took on the character of a certain insidiousness. He was the same way even on exams, in consequence of which the students feared him as fire—once I even happened to see one of my friends at an examination hiding under a bench so as not to be called out after the massacre undergone by his alphabetical predecessor.[8] His malicious manner of examining was of course not to our liking, but we could not help but like his corresponding style of lecturing, and for me personally Ivan Timofeyevich was one of the most interesting professors. Only fragments of comparative anatomy were imparted to us (the digestive organs, circulation of the blood, respiration and locomotion), but these in themselves were so beautiful and were stated so clearly that in the second year I dreamed of the future not about physiology, but about comparative anatomy. It would have been another matter if Ivan Timofeyevich had lectured on physiology according to Johannes Müller's famous textbook, which was in existence at that time; but this did not happen—he apparently confined himself to French authors. I came to this conclusion from the fact that in his lectures no mention was made that physiology was applied physiochemistry, and also from the fact that the frog did not appear in demonstrations and nothing was said about electrical stimulation of nerves and muscles although Germany was long ago full of these experiments

[8] This year Glebov's doctoral examination of a young dissector in anatomy, B., provoked many discussions among the students. He drew a very simple card on the coagulation of blood, but probably became very frightened because having said "If we take a small staff" (Glebov's treatise on the coagulation of blood had begun with these words), he fell silent and could not answer the two questions of the professor which then followed: What would happen if one took the staff and what if one did not take the staff? Not receiving an answer to the last question, the professor showed him the bad mark by his name in the list and said to him: "That's what will happen."

(in 1850 occurred Helmholtz's famous measurement of the speed of conduction along the nerve). We did not even learn from his lectures about such a fact as the stopping of the heart by stimulation of the vagus nerve. The only experiments I remember were: killing a dog before our eyes by insufflation of air in the veins, a demonstration on it of the milk vessels, a long row of pigeons with pinholes in the brain (the pinholes were made by Glebov's assistant, Orlovskiy), which were given to us so that we might describe the disturbances in locomotion and changes in sensitivity caused by the operation.

Professor Lyaskovskiy gave pharmacognosy, and was probably bored with this subject which offered little diversion for him (he had studied abroad under Liebig at Giessen, and under him worked on the follow-up of Mulder's protein theory), because he also gave the lectures in a complete course of qualitative analysis with demonstrations.

Govortovskiy gave organic chemistry.

The professor of pathological anatomy Aleksey Ivanovich Polunin, who in the second year lectured once a week in general pathology and therapeutics introduced us to the field of medicine.... As a pupil of Rokitanskiy, Aleksey Ivanovich was an adherent to humoral pathology, and his lectures consisted essentially in an enumeration of general methods of treatment established by the Viennese school; he did not generally like to enter upon a discourse.

Among the medical students Aleksey Ivanovich was considered almost the best scholar among the medical professors; he, it seems published the medical newspaper, was at almost all the public debates (which were then conducted in Latin) as a critic and generally had a reputation as an extremely exacting worker. . . . Regarding Aleksey Ivanovich's industry, I had occasion to hear praise for him from his university comrade, Professor Nikolayev of children's diseases. The latter was the household physician in the home of Danila Danilych Schumacher, and recounting his student days there he mentioned that he and Aleksey Ivanovich were not only in the same course, but even studied together. According to his words, studies generally were difficult for Aleksey Ivanovich, but he always overcame them with persistent work and patience. Thus, the mechanism of the head's eruption upon coming out of the pelvis in childbirth did not come to him for about two weeks, but nevertheless in the end he understood it. I was a witness to this story, and I attest that it was filled with Nikolayev's sincere intention to render praise to his comrade.

Professor Armfeldt, who lectured to us on encyclopedia of medicine, in his lectures gave the impression of being a very intelligent and educated man, behaved like a gentleman, talked quietly in an even voice (even a little monotonously) so that his talk, put down word for word, could have been printed without corrections. I remember that the general sense of his lectures was as follows: referring to our voluntary acceptance and our sacred duty in the future to serve mankind's ills, he reviewed the range of sciences taught us as a means of attaining the goal, and honestly promised to those who worked, the feeling of fulfillment of a duty in reward, and to those who distinguished themselves—to study abroad. It is remarkable that I do not remember at all his lectures on forensic medicine; I only know that having acquainted us with the form of the legal health certificate, he asked that each of us write on a theme chosen by us ourselves; and even this trifle I remember thanks only to the certificate which I wrote and which was, so to speak, my first writing experience.

In my fifth year I lived in Myasny Lane, on Drachevka, and across the street from the windows of my room opening on the lane, in a little house with a mezzanine, I often saw at the window at work a pretty girl who sat always sideways to the window and worked, not raising her head. With respect to her sitting sideways to the window and never turning to face the street, the thought came to me more than once that she probably had some defect on the side of her face which remained hidden to the observer from the street. This thought served as the design for my written certificate. Sitting opposite me, the girl turned into a poor seamstress with a very beautiful left half of her face and with a big birthmark on her right cheek; a handsome and enterprising youth settled in the apartment opposite her window who was carried away with the seamstress' beautiful profile and of course began approaches. Unfortunately for the girl, she fell deeply in love with this youth, admiring him through the curtained window and hearing his honeyed speech. For all that, in the end he saw her hideous right cheek and was so heartless that he began to laugh at the sight and stopped his attentions and the poor girl lost her mind and was made the object of forensic-medical investigation.

The first two years I studied very diligently and led a sober life in all respects, but on passing to the third year I went off on the wrong track both from medicine and from my sober way of life. The fault of my faithlessness to medicine was that I did not find what I had expected in it—instead of theory there was bare empiricism.

Professor Nikolay Silych Toporov's lectures on particular pathology and therapeutics served as the first push towards this—lectures on the subject which seemed to be the most important. He recommended to us the French textbook of Grisolle and in his lectures he often quoted him with the words "our author." Having bought this book and begun, as far as I remember, with a description of diseases, I read . . . and was amazed—there was nothing in the book except an enumeration of the causes of diseases, symptoms of diseases, their results and methods of treatment, but not a word about how the illness develops from the cause, in what is its essence, and why one or another medicine helps in the disease. I thought: evidently Nikolay Silych and Grisolle are out of date; just let me go to the medical genius Aleksey Ivanovich Polunin and ask him what book I should study. Aleksey Ivanovich actually disapproved of Grisolle and said to me "Take Kanshtatt's work." I ran to the only German bookseller at that time, Deibner (I think on B. Lubyanka), and I found out there that Kanshtatt's work cost 30 rubles, no more, no less—this for a student living on pennies! There was nothing to do, I stayed with Grisolle, and it was a blessing to me because I soon found out that even in Kanshtatt there was not much in the line of questions which interested me. However, it is necessary to do justice to Nikolay Silych's lectures: for those like myself who did not expect the theory of diseases from him, they could even be instructive because he had a large practice,[9] he spoke a great deal about the interesting cases he had seen.

It is clear that even in the lectures on pharmacology and prescription, which were read in Latin by our dean Nikolay Bogdanovich Anke, nothing was said about how medicines act upon the organism—experimental toxicology had just begun to develop at this time in Germany: at best it was only mentioned against which symptoms of a disease a given remedy was used; usually a description was concluded with the phrase: such-and-such a substance is *maxime laudatur* for use in such-and-such diseases. Yet it is well that Nikolay Bogdanovich in his lectures strictly held to Osterlen's German textbook, recommended to us. Acquiring it as I did, the study of pharmacology could be put off until the spring of the following year, i.e., until the transitional examinations. But for those of my comrades who already imagined themselves as future practitioners, the lectures on pharmacology were very important: they carefully wrote out the dictated prescriptions and doses; some were really carried away with the acquired ability of writing prescriptions with their signature in Latin letters.[10]

Professor Basov (I do not remember his first name), well known for being the first in Europe to produce a fistula of the stomach in a dog (with what

[9] Later when Botkin and I were recalling our student days, he always spoke of Nikolay Silych as a very intelligent man and a good practitioner. He justified his certain backwardness with the words as if of Nikolay Silych himself: "Why should we have thermometers and microscopes, it would be clever; we even acquired Toporovka without them (on Little Molchanovka were Toporov's two houses, and the medical men nicknamed this street Toporovka).

[10] Yunge and I, when we finished our doctoral examinations, invited Nikolay Bogdanovich to dinner, entertained him with his favorite port and heard many gay descriptions of university events. One of the stories touched upon his father-in-law, who lived at the Smolensk market place. Nikolay Bogdanovich was a marksman, and his father-in-law, posing as the same, came back from a hunt, however, with none other than a hare or a bird, bought in the market. Once Nikolay Bogdanovich invited his father-in-law to go hunting together in the bushes beyond Dorogomilov. Having brought him to the place, Anke drew off to one side and hid in the bushes. He heard a shot. What is this? Ivan Karlovich has killed a hare. Well done, I say. We approached. Really, there is a dead hare, and between its teeth is a slip of paper. Ivan Karlovich unfolded the paper and read: "Hello, Ivan Karlovich."

goal I do not know), gave the third subject in the third year. He lectured from his own lithographed notes, where everything concerning disease was broken up into small points under numbers. It happened that the bell which ended the lecture would stop it, for example, on the eleventh point of an enumeration of disease symptoms. Then in the following lecture Basov, sitting down on the chair, would scratch his lower lip, smile, and begin: the twelfth . . . i.e., he would begin from the point to which the preceding lecture had lead. I must say that the lecturing took place without any demonstration and without the least rise in tone. He also gave ophthalmology in the same character. To show how the surgeon's hand works in an operation for removal of a cataract he wrapped up a sponge in a handkerchief, imparted to this object squeezed in his left hand a spherical mould, and with his right hand he produced all the surgical developments. I almost failed at his doctoral examination. I received iridotomy and enumerated all points down to the next to the last one; but the last one had slipped my memory, and I paused. The question followed: "What else?" I thought and thought, and finally it dawned on me: "Vomiting." This was the last point in his studies on the after-effects of an iridotomy, not invariable, but sometimes happening, and very dangerous.

Such was my first acquaintance with the so-called principal, theoretical, medical subjects, which disappointed me in medicine as a science. I had no interest in studying them; guidance in all three subjects was for forthcoming examinations, and I began to study outside things.

This year almost next to the auditorium (in the new building) where Toporov, Anke and Basov lectured, the history of the Reformation was being given by Petr Nikolayevich Kudryavtsev; and I listened to all of this course with the same delight with which I later read his *Roman Women according to Tacitus* in *The Archways*, published by Leont'yev. I remember even now his worn, pale face, his look, uncertainly directed into space, as if inspired, and his quiet, beautiful speech when he described the struggle in the monk-ascetic Luther's soul. I heard Granovskiy only once, but he impressed me far differently than Kudryavtsev. I am sorry that I did not write down my impressions at the time—now, after 50 years, I remember only faint traces of them.

Having freed myself from the study of medicine in the third year, I began studying psychology. Among the Vizar family's usual Sunday visitors was a student of the natural science department, Mikhail Ivanovich Ivanov, a great admirer of Rull'ye. From him I learned of the existence of the German psychologist Beneke, whose works, so to speak, established in Moscow University by Katkov, excited the curiosity of Rull'ye and became a subject of enthusiasm of the latter's admirer, Mikhail Ivanovich. His stories aroused in me an interest in psychology; I bought two of Beneke's works: "Psychologische Skizzen" and "Erziehungslehre," and I stuck to the first of them so tenaciously that I was plunged up to the ears in philosophical questions to the point where they finally began to tease me at Danila Danilovich Shumakher's as if I would prove, according to Hegel that light and dark were one and the same thing. Be that as it may, having read Beneke, where the whole picture of psychological life came out of the primary forces of the soul, and not knowing a rebuff to this extreme from the side of physiology, which presented itself to me only much later, I could not but become an extreme idealist, and remained such right up until I left the university. I remember this by the following occurrence. When I was in the fifth year I once received an invitation from Professor Pikulin (he was married to the sister of S. P. Botkin and knew about me, of course, from the latter) to his place for an evening gathering, where among the guests were Professor Min and the then publisher of the *Moscow Gazette* Eugene Korsh (the father of the present-day academician). This evening there were heated psychological discussions. Min was a follower of the encyclopedists, and carried this to the point that he considered psychics as originating in the brain in the same way that bile originates in the liver, but Eugene Korsh and I were defenders of idealism.

However, a passion for philosophical idealism did not save me from enthusiasm in the material aspect. The serpent-tempter for Dmitriy Vizar and myself was Apollon Grigor'yev. Essentially a kind, intelligent and simple man, in spite of a certain theatrical way of Mephistophelizing, with an incomparably greater literary education than we students, lively and greatly interested in discussions, he brought to the Vizars' Sunday evenings much of the animation of his nervous, glib speech, and we could not but like him, the more so because, though he was many years older than we, he conducted himself with us in a comradely fashion, without any pretensions. How he was in his writings, collaborating in the *Muscovite*, I do not know, but at the gatherings at the Vizars' he was neither an enemy to the Westernizers nor an inveterate Slavophile,[11] worshiped only the moral valor of the Russian people and liked only to recite some corresponding verses of Nekrasov, often marvelling how he could write such delightful things. . . . Primarily, he made a fuss over his friend Ostrovskiy, considering him the rising, bright star of the Russian theater. This year, when Ostrovskiy had just written *Poverty Is Not a Vice* he read his production still as a manuscript in the home of Grigor'yev's father, where we were invited by Apollon. In the Vizars' apartment (Zhemochkin's home, near the Don monastery) with a very big hall, he himself arranged a domestic play, *The Misfortune of Being Clever*. In this play he himself played

---

[11] In the nineteenth century, Russian writers could not agree on how Russia should best be reformed. The Slavophiles felt Russia's problems were caused by too much foreign (particularly Western) influence. The Westernizers felt Russia would progress and benefit by more contact with the West and Western concepts of enlightenment and freedom. *Translator*

the role of Famusov and Zagoretskiy, Almazov was Chatskiy, Grigor'yev's wife Elizaveta Fedorovna, born Korsh—Sofiya, Vizar's older sister—Liza, Dm. Vizar—Molchalin, and I—Skalozub.

All of these favors concerned one of the ladies of the Vizars' circle, to whom Grigor'yev was attracted. In her company he was always sober and made himself out to be an intelligent, slightly disillusioned young man, but in the company of young men he appeared in his true form—a debauching student.

At that time a well known lover of Russian songs, Tertiy Ivanovich Filippov (afterwards state controller), lived in Moscow and opened a place there, in part of a wineshop on Tver Street, with an excellent Russian singer and guitarist. Apparently on his recommendation this wineshop also became the place of pilgrimage of the lovers of the Russian nationality, especially those who had no objection to drinking-up to the sounds of the songs of the national drink; and our leader belonged to such a class. At that time when Grigor'yev acquainted us with this entertainment establishment he was there himself and could enter it through the back way after the wineshop had been long closed to the public. Here we became acquainted with a friend of Grigor'yev's, a state-supported student, Rudnev, and through him, with his whole crowd of companions living in Chernyshevskiy apartments, in Theater Square. Here we sat up till late at night over noisy conversations, and drink flowed galore. I remember that once (this was in the spring of 1854, the day before Ascension) Vizar and I left there in the morning in sunshine to accompany Rudnev to the student rooms in the old building of the university. But this was very likely the last act of my merrymaking life, taking place just in a period of transitional examinations. All year I had not looked at my medical books, and I had to apply myself so much to them during the examinations that I had to apply leeches against a rush of blood to the head. I remember this from an incident with the doctor's assistant, who applied the leeches for me. When he finished the operation he wanted to go off to a cozy spot in the yard of our home, and not finding such a place, he found himself in the corner jealously guarded by a vicious dog, Belka. As a result, his trousers were torn and there were distinct teeth marks on the calf of the poor doctor's assistant. These were shown to me with the object that I testify in his behalf in court since the landlord of the house refused to pay him for the mutilation, having found out that he was wounded in an unbecoming spot.

Now, as I am finished with the main episodes of my life in the third year, it would be appropriate to mention my friendship with the family of Danila Danilovich Shumacher, where Vladimir Yakovlevich Vizar took me, I think, in 1853. Danila Danilovich was serving at that time on the council of tutors, a higher official than V. Vizar, and they were great friends. Shumacher's family at that time consisted of the two—he himself and his wife Yuliya Bodanovna, the sister of Granovskiy's wife. On Fridays Vladimir Vizar, Aleksandr Nikolayevich Afanas'yev, the student Sergey Petrovich Botkin and I always gathered at their place. It was here that my acquaintance began with the latter, which passed on into friendship during our stay abroad. Our evenings at tea and supper were very lively. The traditions of Stankevich's circle were well preserved here; much was said about the remaining members of the above-mentioned, about the crank Ketcher and Sergey Petrovich's older brother, Vasiliy Petrovich Botkin (a traveller about Spain), about his fancies and his role in the Botkin family; of course we used to talk about the university, which was then in great disgrace with the authorities. Afanas'yev was the life of the party in this little circle. He was generally an interesting storyteller and laughed killingly at his own stories somehow through his huge nose, and serving in some archives, he found there much that was amusing to the delight of the landlady, who liked very much to listen to gay things. I remember, for example, his story of how Empress Elizaveta went on pilgrimages, and also about some court procession on horseback. Sergey Petrovich was, in his turn, very gay company, and always echoed Afanas'yev, who was his Russian teacher in Einem's boarding school, where Botkin studied prior to his entering the university.

In the fourth year I stopped merrymaking and diligently began visiting the clinics on Rozhdestvenka. Here they put patients on our hands, like curators, and we had to keep a history of the illness in Latin. Therefore I think the phrase "Status idem" was found in our histories much oftener than it should have been, the more so since the professors were hardly interested in the entries we made, and the clinics' assistants at that time even less, since they were not at all concerned with the pursuits of the students. Beyond care, duty of the students was established in the therapeutic and obstetric clinics, but it was so unenforced that I, for example (I was not a student, however, but an auditor), did not have occasion to be on duty a single time in either.

The director of the therapeutic clinic was the then famous Moscow practitioner Over—a person who was decorated with an innumerable quantity of orders, but who did not show his face in his own clinic. During the whole year he gave us only one lecture at the bedside of a patient, and even that was in Latin. His adjunct Mlodzeyevskiy managed the clinic.

We came to this clinic at 8 o'clock in the morning and waited for the professor in a room which served as an auditorium. Mlodzeyevskiy sat down in front of our benches, beside him stood the student on duty the previous day, and the latter's report about the new patients who had come while he was on duty was begun; for this it was necessary to describe the build and age of the patient, his way of living and occupation, the probable cause of his disease, the symptoms found, and the treatment prescribed.[12] After this the professor began his round, accompanied by his assistant and the students. If an important change in the condition of an old patient was noticed, from the words of the assistant, then the professor verified what was said, and he examined the most interesting of the new arrivals in our presence, made a diagnosis, and prescribed treatment. All our training, strictly speaking, consisted in this. They taught us the only method existing in those days (of course, besides looking at the tongue and feeling the abdomen and pulse with the hand) of examining a patient, tapping and listening to the chest, in this clinic, in words, during the rounds, letting us practice both the skills independently, without any guidance. With this aim many students went in the clinic in the afternoon and disturbed the patients a great deal. If there happened to be among the sick women, young women of the Moscow petty bourgeois, then the lovers of females joined the lovers of auscultation and percussion and drove these patients to the silliest airs and politeness with their urbanities. I had the misfortune of having care of such a person and treated her without obligingness. She paid me for this almost with defiance and answered my questions about her health so reluctantly that once I was even forced to remark to her that I was bothering her with these question in the way of duty and that she had to answer me as the person appointed to look after her.

The director of the surgical clinic was Fedor Ivanovich Inozemtsev, the most likeable and most talented of the professors in the medical department. He belonged to those surgeons who do not place the operation first and foremost, but side by side with the preparation of the patient for it and the treatment following the operation. Therefore, he advocated that the surgeon must be a therapeutist. In his clinical lectures we heard first that in certain epochs a definite *Genius morborum* comprising the basic feature of all diseases in general always prevailed. Thus, in the days of Bruss the inflammatory pattern prevailed, in his own words, but at the present time the primarily poor nourishment of the body was observed, with catarrhs of the mucous passages, and consequently the nodulous system of all people in general suffers in managing nourishment. Fedor Ivanovich obviously carried the last idea away from the school bench, but how he arrived at the connection of catarrhs with the sufferings of the sympathetic nerve I do not know. In any case he stubbornly

---

[12] I cannot but recall one very original report done by our comrade, student B., a Caucasian. While the subject concerned men, the matter went satisfactorily; but in the last report about a woman omissions turned up which brought from the professor the observation that in women's diseases the sexual life plays a very important role, and a series of corresponding questions: Is the patient single or married?—Married. Does she have children?—Yes. When was her last child?—Before her wedding. Much later I heard, nevertheless, that B. had a good practice in Tiflis.

believed in this idea and persistently fed all the patients in his clinic sal-ammoniac as a panacea against catarrh, sometimes saying in his lectures that they even teased him with "salmanika" (in prescriptions sal-ammoniac was called in Latin *Sol. ammoniarum*).[13] Although the idea about the sympathetic nerve's influence on the nourishment of the body was rather shattered than proved by physiological analysis at the time when Fedor Ivanovich raised before us the suffering of the nodulous system in *Genius morborum*, nevertheless as a surgeon and an old practitioner it was excusable for him not to know this; consequently, the theory he formed was not worse than the other medical theories, and in any case it was indicative, in Fedor Ivanovich, of a thinking doctor who had given himself over to serious questions. The book he published spoke about milk treatment in the same aspect.

More a Frenchman than a Russian in appearance (it seems he was married to a French woman), living according to nature, he sometimes got carried away in his clinical lectures, and then his phrases took on an impetuous, exclamatory character and were then uttered with a French stylishness. My good impression from his whole figure and speech was made stronger by his extremely affectionate and sympathetic attitude towards the patients, for whom he had no other name than "friend" or "my dear."

In lectures on operative surgery he was entirely another man, he lectured more monotonously than with animation. At that time there was no chair of topographical anatomy, and he had to describe the layered topography of the different regions of the body. How he was as a surgeon we did not succeed in finding out because there was not one major operation this year, and he gave his assistant the minor ones. His assistant was Ivan Petrovich Matyushenkov, well known to us for his out-patient consultations at Inozemtsev's clinic and as a lecturer in minor surgery. Of all our teachers he alone was able to produce on the students a comical impression, with the sharp contrast between his figure and his ways of a coarse, little educated seminarist and with the appearance of erudition which he imposed upon himself in our presence when he fulfilled official duties. This mask so little went with his inner makeup that instead of an intended, erudite seriousness, a grimace of sullen concern came out which passed with the minutes into rage (he was, however, not an unkindly man by nature). These contrasts affected especially keenly the out-patient dispensary, where he was a worker and teacher. At the out-patient clinic there was a small room without seats that compelled the students to stand in two rows like a corridor along the entire length of the room,

[13] They said that the firmness of Fedor Ivanovich's faith in sal-ammoniac was supported by his assistants in his practice, called "the young Inozemtsevs," to whom he gave bread and who constantly brought him news about the marvels of this means. Whether or not this is true I do not know, but it is true that poor Fedor Ivanovich did not know how to choose people and was surrounded in the clinic by indifferent assistants.

straight from the entrance door. At the head of the corridor stood a table with instruments and Ivan Petrovich with a towel across his shoulder, with a sullen, preoccupied face and bowed head. They let the patients into the corridor one at a time, and in the intervals between their entering Ivan Petrovich paced up and down the length of the corridor telling us what we saw and what he was doing. When a patient with a whitlow on his hand showed up in the corridor, which happened most often, Ivan Petrovich, looking at the hand and turning from the patient toward the table with the instruments, said in an offhand manner not looking at anyone: "teneatis fortsius" (I give this phrase in Russian on purpose so that the reader can understand how Ivan Petrovich pronounced Latin); the students nearest the patient stood by his side, but Ivan Petrovich, holding his right hand with a knife behind his back, again approached the patient, saying to him kindly: "Show me your hand, mother;"[14] he made a sign to the students with his head and they seized the patient and a heart-rending cry usually was heard in the room. After this operation Ivan Petrovich invariably said: "In such cases, mothers, it is always necessary to cut the finger to the bone.[15]

In the lectures on minor surgery he was supposed to talk about dislocations and fractures, but he said nothing about this important subject, and the time was devoted most of all to the application of various bandages on a model. In his course, in part, came the description of the procedure of tying vessels, and a description of ligatures preceded this: "Ligatures, mothers, are of two kinds—animal and vegetable; to the first belong intestinal strings, and to the second—silk (sic) and simple threads." I heard this in his lectures with my own ears.

Much later I had occasion to listen to a great deal that was comical about his academic travels abroad, how he had taken it into his head to study inflammation of the mucous membranes and dwelled on the fact that he had put acetic acid in a rabbit's eyes; how he allegedly visited the Brussels (his own name for this city) of Donders, who lived, moreover, in Utrecht. About Botkin and myself, when we were already professors, he spoke thus: they pick at frogs' bones and write about it.

The director of the obstetrical clinic was Professor Koch. It was not obligatory for students to attend it—only those on duty were admitted there, one at

---

[14] He was in the habit of saying to us in the lectures "mothers;" and for a lone sick person—"mother;" therefore he was nicknamed "mother" among the students.
[15] During the recess before the fifth year I had occasion to be in the country twice as a pupil of Ivan Petrovich. The first time was for poor dear Nasten'ka, who was suffering from a huge carbuncle in the small of the back which had tormented her for two weeks before I came. She, poor thing, received from me two huge cross-shaped cuts, and she bore the pain heroically. But the other woman, with a whitlow on her finger, after the cut according to Ivan Petrovich's prescription, threw herself on the ground and began to roll, with cries of "He killed me, he killed me." She was assuaged with difficulty.

a time, and by their own wish. I was not such a volunteer and did not go to the clinic a single time. For this reason I remember Professor Koch only as a lecturer. As far as one may judge a professor by his lectures, Koch was, I believe, the best, or at least the most efficient of the medical department's professors of the time. His lectures had an exceptionally business-like character and were given with that accentuation by which the listener involuntarily recognized in the speaker a master of his subject. I also remember his fine figure, always elegantly dressed for his lectures—always in a black dress-coat in contrast to all the other professors, who were not otherwise than in uniforms.

This year, besides the visit to the clinic, my closest friends Yunge and Einbrodt and I succeeded, thanks to a third friend, dear, kind Pföhl, in practicing surgical operations on a corpse. Pföhl's father was chief doctor in the military hospital (in Lefortov) and gave his son every Sunday a corpse and instruments for surgical practice. Young Pföhl invited us to this. I remember that we studied most all amputations, the bandaging of arteries in various regions of the body and catheterization; on finishing our work I invariably performed the operation of skinning the thigh. Fedor Ivanovich Inozemtsev somehow found out about this and predicted that it meant that I would sometime have to perform this terrible operation on a living person. Fortunately, this prediction did not come true.

This very year I satisfied myself that I was not meant to be a doctor, and I began to dream about physiology. Diseases, by their mysteriousness, did not stimulate the least interest in me since there was no clue to understanding their meaning, and I still could not develop a taste for thinking over these mysteries with the purpose of discerning the essential and the side issues in them—the principal enticement of the true lovers of medicine.[16] On the other hand, I began to be acquainted with physiology this year from the most delightful book of Bergmann and Leikart, *Anatomisch. physiologische Uebersicht des Thierrichs.* Of all the books from my student days I kept this one alone, and to this day I consider this work delightful. At that time it produced on me such a strong impression that I got Vizar's family interested in

---

[16] S. P. Botkin possessed all these qualities in a high degree when he was a professor. For him healthy people did not exist, and each person who came to him interested him almost first of all as a sick person. He looked closely at the walk and at the facial movements, listened, I believe, even to the conversation. Shrewd diagnosis was his passion, and he practiced his acquisition of methods as much as an artist like Anton Rubenstein practiced his skill before a concert. Once, in the beginning of his career as a professor, he took me as an appraiser of his skill in distinguishing the sounds of a small hammer on the plessimeter. Standing in the middle of a large room with tightly closed eyes, he ordered himself turned round several times longitudinally so that he would not know the position in which he stopped, and then knocking on the plessimeter with the small hammer, he recognized whether the plessimeter was turned toward the solid wall, toward the wall with the window, toward the open door, in the other room, or even toward the stove with its door open.

it, and once I even gave a kind of lecture there about the progressive com-
plication of vital manifestations.

In the winter of 1855 before Shrovetide, they collected us fourth-year students in an auditorium of the old university, the dean, Nikolay Bogdanovich
appeared and declared that according to the highest command all of us would
have to take our final examinations and then set off for war; and in the second
week of fast, Emperor Nikolay passed away and it was announced that only
the students with state support would be destined for graduation. I know that
among the latter was the student Kudrin, now the first medical man in the
navy.

Now I shall turn back to describe how the way was paved for the event
which took place in the Vizar family during Shrovetide, 1855.

When I was in the second year, there came to Moscow my best friend in
the engineering college and in the field-engineers, Mikhail Nikolayevich
Vladykin, who was already a retired officer. He had happened to tell me that
he was a passionate theater-goer. So that he could enjoy Shakespeare he was
studying English: then, having read much of Gogol' and Ostrovskiy, he made
up his own comedy of merchant life and retired with the idea of devoting himself to the theatrical art. Now he brought his comedy to Moscow to read it
to Prov Mikhaylovich Sadovskiy. The play was approved by the latter; only
the title was changed, on his advice, and it went under the name of *The
Merchant-Corn Dealer*, it seems, in Shumskiy's benefit performance. Of
course, I saw Prov Mikhaylovich many times on stage, but thanks to Vladykin's friendship with him, I succeeded in seeing him once at a party at
Vladykin's and hearing one of his famous stories—"The Tale of Captain
Kopeykin." Vladykin sat by Prov Mikhaylovich's side and listened to him
with such strained attention that when Captain Kopeykin during his story
turned to his neighbor, screwing up his eyes, with the question what his opinion was about that which had just been said, Vladykin involuntarily answered
the question and of course provoked the irrepressible laughter of the whole
audience. To continue Captain Kopeykin was impossible, but other stories
soon took its place. Later, through Vladykin, I became acquainted with
another famous storyteller, Gorbunov.

After *The Corn Dealer* was played on the stage, Vladykin continued to
write, lived the greater part of the time at his own place in the country, but
he began to come to Moscow every year. On one of these visits I introduced
him to the Vizar family.

When I was in the third year, in the second half of the year, Leonida
Yakovlevna (the older sister), a very young, lively, beautiful girl with jet-
black hair and light blue eyes, passed an examination for the rank of teacher
and went to work in Frolov's family, for his grown daughters, as a friend-

Frenchwoman. She passed a year there, and in the winter of 1855 she went back home to Zhemochkin's home, near the Don Monastery. All the young people who came to this house felt, of course, a certain soft spot for this kind girl, and I, too, belonged to these, of course not showing it. And judging by conversations, Vladykin also suffered the same soft spot towards her, but nothing came of this because he saw her from time to time, for hours. But when Shrovetide in 1855 drew near, Vladykin was in Moscow, and I was with him at Zhemochkin's home every Sunday and learned in one of these visits that the head of the house, Vladimir Yakovlevich, through some friends had arranged a place for his sister as a governess in a very good family in Kazan' and that poor Leonida Yakovlevna would go there at Lent. Returning to town with Vladykin from this soirée, I elaborated on the sad fate awaiting the poor girl, and as a close childhood friend, I told him directly that he alone might save her from this fate by marrying her. However, there was no need to persuade him because the news of her forthcoming disappearance apparently had a very strong effect on him, and I only had to encourage good Vladykin. Be that as it may, on the last day of Shrovetide we were at Zhemochkin's home again and here, for the sake of the festive day, a dance was arranged[17] in which both retired field-engineers took part. I saw with my own eyes how after the quadrille was over Vladykin stood at Leonida Yakovlevna's chair, how she blushed with tears welling up in her eyes, hurriedly left the room and returned after a minute blushing and shining. The fast of the bride and bridegroom was of course gay, but at the end of it Vladykin was called into the militia, and they married only after I had finished my year, when I was abroad. When they were married they went on a long trip around Europe, to Spain, and then lived in the country (Vladykin was district marshal of nobility), and then in Moscow, where he went on the stage. Still later both lived abroad, while she studied medicine in Bern, where she finished the course. Still later Vladykin wrote another theatrical play, "The Pool," went all over the Caucasus as a hunter, and portrayed it. All this was, and now, for a long time, both have been gone. I met Leonida Yakovlevna when I was an old man when I left Petersburg for Moscow, where she lived, practicing medicine. We met, of course, as friends, but fate did not let us continue this new friendship for long—disease consumed her; she knew the disease was fatal and died a hero. All my memories of good moments in my student days are connected with the memory of her sweet, modest appearance. Besides her I knew one more very sweet, clever girl with whom I became acquainted thanks to the fact that on her mother's side she was of the Pazukhin family, and I was introduced to her

[17] The young Vizar girls had four friends: three sisters—French girls (to whom I gave lessons in arithmetic when they were preparing for the teachers' examination) and a very intelligent girl, Lizanka Freimut, who later studied entomology with great success and even wrote a treatise on flies.

by her aunts, our neighbors in the country. The aunts spoke to me about their niece, Naden'ka Shneyder, with the highest praise, and she indeed was worthy of this with her intellect, kindness, and sweet disposition. I was not there often, but thanks to the fact that her relatives introduced us to each other and thanks to the simplicity inherent in both of us we quickly became close friends.

The clinics during the fifth year were in the Yekaterininskaya hospital on Strastnyy Boulevard. At the head of therapeutics was Professor Varvinskiy and his assistant, Pikulin, and surgery—Professor Pol', his assistant Popov, and an elderly assistant Novatskiy.

Varvinskiy, as far as I remember, did not give clinical lectures and worked only at listening to the curators' accounts of the illness of patients assigned to them, correcting and clearing up mistakes in these accounts. I also remember his bad way of regarding the patients' fancies and the students' mistakes in the defined disease with a grin. By his manner he made many students very embarrassed. One of our comrades, good Korobkin, blind in one eye, a stutterer, especially suffered from him. The professor should properly have spared the poor fellow and not drawn him for torment, but Varvinskiy enjoyed it when he, red and breathless, made efforts and stammered over the patients. He also loved to talk with the student Fisher after the latter had not succeeded once in diagnosing intermittent fever. Pikulin was at odds with his own patron, and went to the clinic only in the evenings, it seems, with the sole purpose of teaching us auscultation and percussion. Students of that time could learn this skill only under him.

The surgical clinic of professor Pol' was, I think, almost one-third filled with children with calculi since Pol' was a great lover of the lithotomy by the method of his brother Yakov, and always performed these operations himself, leaving the rest to his assistant Popov. On his daily round of the patients Pol' always came with sweets in his pocket, and behind him went his assistant with a cup of butter. The sweets served for calming the children while the professor examined them *per rectum*. Professor Pol' was at that time already a very elderly person, and his assistant, Popov, actually managed the clinic, but he apparently troubled not so much about earthly matters as about the saving of souls. I heard this from my comrade Yunge. Pol' liked him very much, and when he found that Yunge was a Lutheran, he strongly advised him to accept Catholicism. About Professor Popov I can only say that he was not infected with sentimentality; he cursed the patients even during an operation, and once before my eyes he gave his assistant a full blow on the ear.

Besides the clinics in the fifth year, pathological anatomy and hygiene were given. I do not remember the contents of Aleksey Ivanovich Polunin's lectures on pathological anatomy; I know only that he showed many pathological preparations and taught the procedure of dissecting corpses. How helpful he was to the students I will not undertake to judge, but he obviously knew how to fill his subordinates with a love for knowledge: his assistant at that time, Aristarkhov, later became a doctor, and even the watchman at the pathological anatomy study, an old retired soldier (a Finn), Ivan Ivanovich, took an interest in knowledge, and taught the students catheterization. Concerning hygiene it will be sufficient to say that there was not such a disgraceful professor in one of the universities, I think, as K. Until we entered the fifth year he was one of the sub-inspectors and was transformed by some miracle all at once into a hygienist. They said that this was the work of the trustee, General Nazimov.

In conclusion I must confess: knowing that I would not be a doctor, I treated my medical studies this year without interest; that is why my recollections about my fifth year are so scanty.

Having finished the course and knowing to myself many faults in medicine, especially practical, I did not think to take the doctor's examination directly, but our dean, Nikolay Bogdanovich Anke, compelled me to do this, saying that the department demanded this without fail. I believed this, but it was not true. Two of his favorites—Yunge and Einbrodt, Germans, came up for their doctorates, probably at his request; but among the medical professors two, Glebov and Basov, were Russophiles, and they did not like it when preference was given in something to Germans before Russians, and were strict at examinations. Therefore Anke had to add to the two Germans one Russian as a candidate to mollify these examiners. They might have been mollified, but not entirely—Glebov nevertheless failed Einbrodt, although the examinations were very simple, differing from those for physicians (like now, however) only in that they made the doctoral candidate answer two extra questions. I later heard that I could have found myself, upon returning from abroad, a professor of physiology not in the Petersburg Medical Academy, but in Moscow University, but I missed thanks only to Nikolay Bogdanovich Anke. The matter was that when Professor Glebov left the chair, which happened probably a year after I went abroad, Anke proposed Einbrodt for his place in order that he be sent at public expense for advanced study in the sciences abroad, and Fedor Ivanovich Inozemtsev proposed me. Then Nikolay Bogdanovich declared that he knew for certain that I was studying not physiology, but psychology, and Inozemtsev's proposal was refused.

In conclusion I cannot but recall the important Moscow events which took place during my student days (1850-1856). This time was especially rich with them.

It is well known that when the revolutionary movement of 1848 and 1849 came close to our borders in Prussia and Austria, Emperor Nikolay found it necessary to take special measures against the penetration of pernicious ideas to us from the West, and one such measure was a reduction in Moscow University (whether this measure was extended also to other universities I do not know) in the number of students in all departments, except the medical, to 300. In 1850 this measure was already in effect, and the head of the university (Alfonskiy) was already installed. Later (I do not remember what year) the department of philosophy, of which Katkov was head, was closed, and in place of this ultraloyal patriot to logic and psychology, Archpriest Ternovskiy began to lecture. At the same time rumors started that some colonel had been appointed to the university to train the students in artillery and for the front. They even talked as if two cannons would be placed in the university. Several of the students perhaps even believed these rumors, but the majority regarded them ironically. Thus, several of my friends advised me jokingly to come forward as a candidate for training students in marching drill. I can imagine what a disturbance similar rumors and measures among the students would provoke now, but at that time the students had not yet come out in a solid mass. The discomfort of the present situation was of course recognized, but conversations about this took place, so to speak, on the sly, in close friends' circles. Among my friends, for example, was a Pole, B., and we often discussed the present situation of things—I grieved over it, but he was of the opinion that the worse it was the better.

I could not be at the celebration of the one-hundredth anniversary of the university (1855) because I was an auditor, and I was told that I could have come to this celebration only in a nobleman's uniform, and even my civil dress was not too good. The whole year I had to sport a coat the color of which led me to be called siskin at the Vizars. Then in fashion in broadcloth was "the color of London fog" and I wanted to have sewn for myself a coat of such a color; but I was so careless as to buy the broadcloth in the evening in a dark shop and received in place of London fog a color almost that of a billiard cover.

The same year Timofey Nikolayevich Granovskiy died. They performed a funeral service for him in the university chapel, and I remember that by the side of his coffin stood his wife, all in black, motionless as a statue the whole time of the service (his wife was born Mulhauzen, a Lutheran). Thousands followed his coffin, but not nearly so solemnly as they later followed Turgenev in Petersburg. Even now among the followers I remember Katkov in a raccoon coat. At that time, however, he was only the publisher of the *Russian Herald*. Had Granovskiy died nine years later, the editor of the *Moscow Gazette* would hardly have gone behind his coffin.

The fire in Moscow's Bolshoy Theater I think was in 1853. During the fire Yunge and I stood beside the present-day Continental Hotel and were witnesses to the rescue of a man from the roof of the theater. The firemen's ladder did not reach this roof, and a worker rescued the man standing on the roof by climbing on the roof (by the ladder at first, of course) by the drainpipe. We could not see the actual procedure of the rescue because it took place on the facade turned towards the passages, but there were witnesses to how someone took it into his head to collect money for the daredevil. Unfortunately the money did him a bad turn: he drank himself to death on it.

When I was in the fourth year our family lost our dear gentle mother. Her meek soul suffered not a little in life, but at least God sent her a peaceful and quick death. I received the news of her death unexpectedly. Thus she, poor one, did not live to the time when her son played the learned role which she had wished so much.

By my father's last will the whole estate passed to mother to be at her complete disposal until death, and father's will was respected. At mother's death the brothers allotted the whole Kostroma estate to the sisters, but decided not to divide the Simbirsk, adding to the agreement the point that any who nevertheless wished to divide would receive 6000 rubles and would renounce any further right to father's inheritance. Intending to go abroad to study I wished to be separate on the stated condition, and received, in addition to that, freedom for my loyal comrade—my servant Feofan Vasil'yevich. Since my final examinations were over at that time, in the beginning of June it was late to go abroad, and therefore in the summer I went to Teplyy Stan to say goodbye to my relatives. Here I had the occasion for the second and last time in my life to give medical help to someone (cutting poor Nasten'ka's carbuncle was the first such case). A big piece of bread gulped down had lodged in a peasant's gullet, and he came to me for help in a great fright. For lack of a probe I got from my sisters' stays the plate of a whalebone, fastened on the end of it a piece of sponge moistened with lamp oil and pushed the stuck piece through. The poor peasant threw himself at my feet with joy. I passed the end of the summer at the Vizar's cottage, saw Emperor Aleksandr II's entry into Moscow before the coronation, and on the very day of the coronation I walked with the Vizars about illuminated Moscow. I still remember that before I left for abroad I bought, on Feofan Vasil'yevich's advice, a gold watch, which he considered an indispensable accessory to a barin. He gave me this advice on the following occasion. When I had finished my studies, my cousin Tukhachevskaya, wishing to give me a gift, summoned Feofan Vasil'yevich to learn from him what I needed most of all. He unhesitatingly suggested "a good gold watch" and since we did not receive one, he decided that we must get one on our own account.

5

STUDIES ABROAD (1856-1860)

WHEN I had received the money from the trustee council, I deposited it with kind, good Vladimir Yakovlevich Vizar, and he sent it to me abroad in installments. I lived there on this money three and a half years, from the fall of 1856 to February 1860. I remember that before I left I received a 1500-ruble letter of credit in the office of the Moscow banker Kovli and in Berlin I received 1575 thalers for this letter of credit. Such was the recognition of the Russian ruble even at that time—and that was after the Crimean campaign!

I left Moscow for Petersburg on the third day of Aleksandr II's coronation with a passport "for illness" and with a payment of 50 rubles for half a year—at that time passport procedures of the time of Nikolay had not yet been repealed. Then two passenger ships on public expense left Petersburg for Stettin, and I went on one of them. The beginning of the voyage was not entirely successful. We had been gone from Kronstadt just two hours when the ship turned back to where it had come from, and they announced to us that we could go to the city until evening since the ship would be loaded with more coal. In Kronstadt I had occasion to be witness to a very typical scene. On one of the town squares I saw standing there a crowd of Russian sailors, onlookers to the struggle of two fighters—a drunk Russian and a sober foreign (judging by his dress) sailor; the Russian stood in a fighting position and the foreigner seized him by the cuffs of his unbuttoned overcoat under the throat; at that moment two friends of the foreigner—one a huge man—apparently pushed their way through the crowd, parted the fighters and freely led their comrade out of the crowd. From this I involuntarily remembered a

65

case of a needless fistfight which I saw on Moscow river between Kamennyy and Krymskiy bridges. The fight had just started between boys of opposite sides when from Kamennyy bridge the uncomely figure of a policeman with a stick raised threateningly began to come near the crowd of more than 100 persons. Seeing this observer of order, the whole crowd scattered.

Be that as it may, towards evening we finished loading and went all the way to Stettin without incident.

The lectures had not begun yet in Berlin, and therefore I took advantage of the free time and went to Dresden; I went on foot about Saxon Switzerland, and from there I went via Prague to Vienna. On the road from Berlin to Dresden an amusing incident took place. In a small compartment for four in the German coaches of that time, an old man and a middle-aged woman—Germans—sat opposite me. Talking to each other, they looked at me very often with such curiosity that it involuntarily aroused in me the desire to behave like a schoolboy. For a long time the old man restrained himself, but finally he could not bear it, and entered into conversation with me. Finding out from my first words that I was a foreigner, he observed questioningly that I had come from overseas and asked if I was from South America. To this I replied: really from overseas, but not from America, but from Persia, by the Caspian Sea. My fellow travelers of course rejoiced at the chance to receive reliable information about Persia, what was the nature of the country and what were the people like there. I probably gave answers satisfactory to them for all of this, and I even recited for them, having an acquaintance with the sounds of the Persian language, some verses which I had studied in my childhood from Marlinskiy's tale "Mulla-Nur," which I passed for verses of Firdousa.

> Gyudul' Gyudul' khom gyal'dy
> Arondyndan yagysh gyal'dy
> Gyalin, alga dur sana
> Chyumganym dal'dur sana.

However, when they asked me what the monetary units were called in Persia (which I do not know even now), I had to evade it by supposed lack of understanding of the question and to answer that it was managed like theirs, gold and silver. Fortunately the good man rescued me, asking if there were not rupees. I agreed, of course, and the matter was ended happily. On parting they advised me to stop at the Berliner Hof hotel, and they must have asked what name I had written down because about two days later I suddenly met my former traveling companion on the street and she greeted me, laughing, with the words: "Hello, Mr. Russian," to which I answered: "No, ma'am, russified Persian."

I must say that I was delighted with the Dresden gallery, with the hitherto unparalleled mountains of wonderful Saxon Switzerland, I walked about the Viennese Prater, was in Stephan's Kirche, and so on. I know that I described all this with great enthusiasm in a letter to my Moscow friends; but this was forty-seven years ago, and however distinctly I recall pictures of this distant past, nevertheless what I experienced at that time—alas—does not come back.

Returning to Berlin, I found there S. P. Botkin, who soon became the person closest to me. He had gone abroad a half year before I did and now came to Berlin after Virchow, who had just moved from Würzburg to the Prussian capital to the anatomical-pathological institute set up for him.

My first steps in laboratory life were very original. I must remark that at that time in Moscow University even though chemistry was given to the medical students, nevertheless they were not permitted in the chemistry laboratory. Therefore when I went to Berlin to the private chemistry laboratory of assistant professor Zonnenshteyn, for the study of qualitative and quantitative analysis I did not even know how to do what is called washing the chemical dishes, and I, a doctoral candidate, had to listen to directions from the laboratory attendant on how to handle fire, dishes, a blowtorch, etc. But apparently the attendant's hand was facile, the matter was quickly put right, and after about two months I could pass on to the laboratory of medical chemistry at the anatomical-pathological institute.

I stayed a year in Berlin (through the fall of 1857), and almost all of this time was spent at studies in two laboratories and listening to lectures: Magnus —in physics, Heinrich Roze—in analytical chemistry, Johannes Müller—in comparative anatomy of the genitals of vertebrates, Du Bois-Reymond—in physiology, and Hoppe—in histology. However, at the end of the 1857 summer session I began collecting experimental material in my spare moments for the dissertation I had planned and studying the literature on the question.

I went abroad with the firm intention to study physiology, and therefore when I arrived in Berlin I was of course drawn most of all to the physiology lectures and the physiology laboratory, but in this respect I was rather disappointed. Three times the celebrated Johannes Müller continued to be the official representative of the department of physiology, but he had long since stopped studying this science, he gave lectures on physiology only in summer sessions, the whole course in three months, and did not admit physiology students. Beside him stood his famous pupil, Du Bois-Reymond; but he was then still an extraordinarius professor; his lectures were not compulsory for the students and were not attended by them, and therefore he read what he wanted, of his own choosing. In such a way, in the winter semester of 1856 he gave in essence a course on electrophysiology with many great detours into innervation of the heart, intestines, and respiratory movements. He had no pupils, and indeed he could not have had any because his laboratory consisted of a single room in which he himself worked (and where no one else had access), and the corridor adjacent to it with a window and a single plain table at the window. Nevertheless, thanks to Doctor Kupfer from Dorpat, who listened to the lectures with me and who wanted to become acquainted in reality with galvanic phenomena in muscles and nerves, Kupfer and I succeeded in studying and doing experiments in the corridor using a Sauerwald galvonometer for physiological purposes, and working with the muscles and nerves of frogs. Also at the professor's wish, we repeated on an eel the experiments on spinal reflexes just published at that time by Pflüger. Of course, so little time was required for all this that the principal place of studies at Berlin became for me the laboratory of medical chemistry just founded at Virchow's institute, with its young director Hoppe-Seyler, a nice, good and lenient teacher who did not differentiate at all between the German and Russian students. The passage from the cold corridor to the warm, comfortable laboratory of Hoppe was for me a joyous event, but I am nevertheless much indebted to Du Bois-Reymond's lectures and the studies in the corridor: becoming acquainted with the sphere of phenomena of which we in Russia did not even have a thought, they gave us the means of advancing easily in the extensive class of phenomena which comprised the later, so-called, general physiology of nerves and muscles. Studies in Hoppe-Seyler's laboratory consisted mainly of a study of the composition of animal fluids and were so brought into the system that the study went easily and quickly. He did not give us Russians, since we were really beginners, special topics, but he willingly heard out the schemes which came into our heads and helped bring them about with advice and deed if the scheme proved to be reasonable and feasible. Thus, he fully approved of the plan I conceived of studying acute alcohol poisoning . . . and in his own laboratory I made: an investigation of expelled air for alcohol, a measurement of the quantity of CO_2 exhaled by an intoxicated animal, the influence of alcohol poisoning on body temperature (in the arteries, veins, and rectum) and intoxication by inhalation of alcohol.

And now a few words about the professors I heard in Berlin, and their lectures—a few words because I saw the professors only from afar, on the chair, and the lectures I heard, for all their intrinsic value, were essentially elementary.

Magnus was considered a first-rate lecturer and an extremely skillful experimenter. Later in Heidelberg I heard a story from Helmholtz in his laboratory, of how Magnus prepared experiments for his lectures. According to this story he always tried to impart to the experiments such a form as to put into action the apparatus shown or evoke the desired phenomenon by means of pulling a string or a tap or any simple movement of the hand in general. There is no doubt that in the Berlin *Urania* which appeared much later the simple physical apparatuses put into action by the hands of visitors by means of pulling a thread were established by a pupil of Magnus. I took a staff course in experimental physics for medical students and students of pharmacy, which was given during the winter semester. The course by necessity was elementary (the complete course of physics in 6.5 months) but it was very luxuriously provided with experiments done with such speed that they did not disturb the smoothness of the reading. Carbonic acid was changed in about a quarter of an hour into lumps of loose snow which were thrown among the listeners in the auditorium.

Heinrich Roze was, as is well known, a celebrated specialist in analytical chemistry and gave his extremely useful, but essentially rather boring, material with the greatest enthusiasm. It was painful to see with what indelicacy the German students behaved at the lectures of the poor old man who suffered with intense hemorrhoids. He was very tall, lectured standing, and from time to time he had to squat heavily behind the chair because of his illness, which always evoked a snicker from the listeners.

Before speaking about Johannes Müller I must remark that having come to Berlin intending to hear university lectures, I thought that one could not do other than enter the university as a student, and I began as such—I presented myself, along with the other students, to the dean at that time, Trendelenburg, heard a preceptorial speech by him, and like all the others, was honored with a handshake. Then I paid the fee for all the above listed courses to the treasurer and, in passing, the fee for studies in the comparative anatomy museum of Johannes Müller. With a receipt from the treasurer one had to report to the professors, and they gave authorization cards. Thus, I had to report to Johannes Müller during his office hours and get permission from him to visit the museum to begin with and study osteology of fish. However, nothing came of these visits; in the room where the attendant let me in there was no one besides me; Johannes Müller did not go there and I did not dare to go to him with questions, and I soon entirely abandoned these visits and also the very thought of comparative anatomy. Nevertheless, from the sole wish to listen to such a celebrity as Johannes Müller I registered in the 1857 summer session for his lectures. I must confess that in my soul was still hidden the naïve habit brought from Moscow of thinking that each famous professor was necessarily a brilliant orator, and I expected to hear in this auditorium an absorbing talk full of wide generalizations, but instead I heard a purely business-like talk with a showing of drawings and alcoholic preparations. This was, however, the last year of Johannes Müller's glorious life, and at the lectures he appeared a tired, ill man. In all his movements and in his very speech a certain nervousness was felt; he lectured quietly, not raising his voice, and only his eyes continued to burn with the indescribable brillance which together with the famous name of the scholar became historical.

That which I expected from Johannes Müller's lectures crept from time to time into the lectures of his celebrated pupil Du Bois-Reymond; I say "crept" because the auditorium was not arranged for oratory. Seven persons in all were at his lectures this semester, and among them were two Russians, Botkin and I. In any case his lectures, both by their content and their execution, were winning. The subject was entirely new for us; the professor's speech flowed smoothly, easily, and his German sounded very beautiful. I especially remember his lecture on the rapidity of conduction of excitation along the nerves. Here he positively got carried away and told with animation the whole story of this discovery: Johannes Müller's doubt about the possibility of measuring so rapid a process, his own thoughts on how one could proceed experimentally on this problem, and finally, the solution of the problem by his friend, the great pupil of the same Johannes Müller, Helmholtz. Describing Helmholtz's myograph, he named the breaking and restoring metallic contact in the form of a mercury filament, the brilliant point of this method. Another time, I do not remember on what occasion, he spoke in his lectures about human races and treated us, his Russian listeners, with the remark that the long-headed race possesses all kinds of talents, but the short-headed, in the best instance, only imitation. If all Russians in general were meant by this, then the opinion was still gracious for a German because during these years we more than once came to feel that the Germans looked upon us as barbarians. While I studied in the corridor, Du Bois-Reymond did not enter into any conversations with me since behind the same table sat a German, Kupfer; but after two years, when I was returning from Helmholtz's laboratory via Berlin to Russia, I had to visit Du Bois-Reymond (I will tell why later), he met me very amicably, and after two more years, when I returned from Paris, even positively kindly.

During the year, with the arrival in Berlin of two new students from Moscow University, a small circle of friends was formed. Good Bekkers, a former surgeon under Pirogov in the Sevastopol' campaign, came, and Yunge, who was in my same year. The first meant to study surgery, and the second— ophthalmology. Later, upon returning from abroad, all four of us found ourselves professors in the Petersburg Medical-Surgical Academy. Studies for Botkin and myself continued from morning until 6 o'clock in the evening (with a one hour break for dinner in Töpfer's medical restaurant); after studies our group very often came together, with the right to enjoy ourselves earned during the day, and we enjoyed ourselves because means for merrymaking for a young man were not few at that time in Berlin. Effervescent Botkin was the life of the party and the leader. Even the elderly Germans liked him, but there is nothing to say about the young ones. He and Bekkers were great lovers of German music, and I of Italian, and therefore twice a week in the evenings they inevitably dragged me along to concerts of Liebig at Krol in Tiergarten as if to correct my poor musical taste. However, I remained a lover of Italian music because the concerts had an ultra-classical character, and Liebig conducted with an ultra-German tranquility. It is apropos to note here that, going abroad, I dreamed of being in beautiful Italy without fail; therefore, I found an Italian teacher in Berlin (an Italian refugee, a former colonel in the service of the Pope, Mr. Kalandrelli) and took lessons from him.

This year I believe we were in all the entertainment places in Berlin, not excluding even the so-called shpitsbals, where, however, we were observers, not taking part in the dances. In its composition it was the same as the Petersburg dance classes of that time (for example the famous dance class of Martsinkevich mentioned by Shchedrin in his essays); but what a terrible difference between them: there was noise, hubbub, and dances almost with somersaults, but here (at least in the dancing hall) sheer well-being. For example, the music began a prelude to the waltz, and the whole audience—a hundred couples, I believe—formed themselves two-by-two after each other along the walls. Then the dance director with a wave of his cocked hat divided the first group of dancers, 25 couples, from the rest, and the separate group began to perform, and the rest quietly awaited their turn while the first group went round. At a new movement of the cocked hat the dancers stopped in a line and the second group began to perform, and so on until the end. And the same dances were performed with measured steps, with a ceremonious execution of all steps. There was no fire, no passion, but what self-command to make up for it!

In the winter of 1856 I became acquainted with the famous Russian artist artist Aleksandr Andreyevich Ivanov. He had come to Berlin for several days to seek Grefe's advice about his eyes. Probably one of S. P. Botkin's older brothers advised him to go to Berlin because he came with a letter for Botkin and in such a way got into our group. He stayed several days and of course could not but leave the most gratifying impression of himself. The following year I met him in Rome, and I will tell about our very long friendship below.

In August of 1857 after summer session, my dream of visiting Italy was finally fulfilled. With this aim I exchanged letters with my university friend, the nicest fellow and great eccentric V., who was teaching at that time in Würzburg. I planned on meeting him in Würzburg and going together to Munich and from there on foot through the Tyrols. Of all my walks about Europe there was not another so fascinating as this one by the richness and variety of impressions which, moreover, have fallen again on cold ground. Also the captivating disposition of my travelling companion brought a very nice lively note to this journey, although in the beginning of the journey he did not cheer me, and I had to comfort him. A half year before in Berlin he had been platonically in love with a certain woman and wept bitterly on saying farewell to her, and in Würzburg was in love, also platonically, with the daughter of the host of the restaurant where he dined, and having parted with her on the railway platform, in the car he was drowned in scalding tears, and hid his face in the corner so that the other passengers would not notice. Fortunately, I did not have to comfort him for long: already in Munich the sufferer as if forgot about Würzburg and was entirely absorbed in working out a detailed plan of the journey on the basis of Bedeker and the information concerning the Tyrolean Sehenswürdigkeiten which he had gathered in Würzburg from natives. Our route lay via Innsbruck and Brenner Pass to Verona, with short side trips.

In Munich, going sightseeing, we were still townspeople, but beyond its limits we were transformed into mountaineers with knapsacks on our shoulders and with the firm intention of renouncing, at V.'s insistence, Russian delicacy in the form of guides, good food, and a soft bed on the way. Knowing from Bedeker where one should go on foot and where one could cheaply take a ride in a "Stellwagen" (a kind of very bad coach), we travelled about Tyrol I believe for ten days and lost our way in the mountains only once, and even then not uselessly since we stayed in a remote Tyrolean village. Shepherds rescued us from our difficulty, showing us the way which went to the village, lying, as it turned out, on the cattle road. We went there to an inn, tired and hungry, had supper—it was already towards evening—of beefsteak occupying a whole frying pan of medium size, with a mountain of potatoes, slept that night in a hayloft, drank coffee in the morning (it is true, it was bad), and for all this we paid a gulden, i.e., 60 kopeks. So there were still such people and places in Europe at that time!

Out of Munich our first halting place was the mountain salt-works of Hallein, where for a very small fee one could walk through the underground galleries which descended from the top of the salt mountain to its base. Here the salt was extracted by leaching the mountain rock, for which great excavations had been made in the mass of the mountain in the form of a room; the exit from it was shut up, and across its entrance the room was filled with water, and remained shut up until the water was filled with salt to a certain percentage. Then the brine was let from the room into a saltpan. In the pits where they took visitors there was a very original means of communication between the upper and lower floors. They put leather trousers on the visitor, a leather glove on the right hand, and a lighted lantern in the left. In this outfit the visitor, at the entrance into the dark pit, sat astride a log, took a firm stand, and lay hold of the cable with his right hand; then the guide's command to release your feet was heard and the rider flew unchecked into the dark abyss sliding on the log, which was as slippery as glass. At the end of the descent the greatly inclined log probably made a gradual curve towards horizontal because the slipping slowed down by itself and almost entirely stopped. This was, of course, the most pleasant part of the underground ride; but at the end of it, at the very lowest part of the pit, new surprises awaited us: a huge cavern with an underground lake illuminated by ten small glasses, a ride on the lake in a boat and disembarkation to a narrow gauge railway along which unseen forces rush you in impenetrable blackness and carry you suddenly into the bright open air.

If I had had the good habit of getting up in the morning with the sunrise I could of course recall a walk very often in the Tyrols in the cool hours of a summer morning, without worries and constraints, with a certain feeling of freedom in my soul. But this was so long ago, and in my soul up to this time there have been so many other similar but more beautiful impression (after 2 years, in the summer of 1859, I had occasion to go on foot, on a trip with Dmitriy Ivanovich Mendeleyev, across the whole "Bernese Oberland"), that from all our wandering through the Tyrols I remember only Berchtesgaden, its slightly dreary, but nevertheless picturesque lake (Königssee) with smart, well-dressed boatwomen and the beautiful snowy mountains in the background of the picture. We walked to Merano and went according to the route drawn up beforehand, but at Merano we met a professor of botany from Würzburg (I believe his name was Schlenk), and on his advice we turned to the right towards the pass across the Alps to the valley of Lago di Como. This pass across Mt. Stelvio (Stiefser Joch) along the Austrian post road at a height of 7000 feet has remained in my memory. I remember that we spent the night at the foot of the mountain, got up with the sunrise, and began to climb at 6 o'clock in the morning. At 12 o'clock we were already at the top of the pass, higher than the line of perpetual snow, with a panorama of snowy mountains around, and on the border of the Italy I so passionately desired. I remember what a joyous feeling came over me with the thought that I was already in Italy and how I set out running for the post station which could be seen not far off. There were different faces here, different dress, the beautiful Italian speech, and even red wine, instead of the beer inevitable up to this time. From here we of course went straight to Colico and then by boat on the lake to Bellagio, which seemed to me an earthly paradise. We stayed here, I believe, two days because we wandered about the neighborhood, visiting, of course, the villa Serbelloni; we rented a boat without a guide and several times the two of us went for a ride. V. was a very skillful swimmer, and on one of these sailings when we were far from shore he took it into his head to swim. No sooner said than done. Quick as always, V. undressed in a minute, piled up his clothes, got up on the side of the boat and threw himself in the lake. After several seconds I heard a desperate shout: "My coat, my money!" I looked, and by the side of the boat was floating in the water, spread out, his ill-fated coat. Fortunately, we succeeded in pulling it out together with his wallet in the side pocket—all of V.'s wealth. Here I said goodbye to my good travelling companion—he longed for Switzerland—and I myself set off via Milan for Venice. I do not remember whether this happened by an agreement or not, but in Milan I met S. P. Botkin and exactly on the day of arrival there of the then Lombard vicegerent, Archduke Maximilian (later the unfortunate Mexican emperor), who had just returned to his post after his marriage. In any case I remember clearly that in the evening I walked with S. P. Botkin along the Milan streets burned by fires, with crowds of people who were singing loud songs; but I left Milan by railroad alone and arrived in Venice at about 10 o'clock in the evening. One must come to this charming city for the first time just at night because during the day, on the first trip along the canals you take pleasure only in the novelty of the visual, and besides, completely distinct impressions, but at night in the dim light of the canals flashing past you with a vague, mysterious form, you are surrounded by an imperturbable quiet, without a single sound except the light splashings of water under the gondolier's oar. You will float really charmed. I stopped at the still prosperous Hotel di Luna because of the enticement of its name and did well because although Piazza San Marco was not visible from the hotel, it was only two steps from it in all, which I of course did not fail to take a few minutes after my arrival. Whoever has been in Venice knows what kind of an impression this square produces on the newcomer in the evening when thousands of lights are burning in the stores and cafes along its long lateral facades, and in the background the outlines, well known from pictures, of the campanile, cathedral, and blacksmiths with their bell stand out against the dark sky. The hotel with the enticing name, however, turned out to be not for my pocketbook, and on the following morning I found an inexpensive furnished room in a remote part of the Riva degli Schiavoni, almost opposite the bath houses which existed at that time. Since childhood I had never gone bathing in the sea, and therefore on the very first day I visited this establishment, which consisted of separate compartments in which one could only stand in the water up to the shoulders, but could not in any way swim. As a person studying chemistry I of course should have known about the incompatibility of soap with sea water, but I forgot about that and turned my hair into a mess of hard tufts. Fortunately, in each cubicle was a pitcher of fresh water, and the matter was put straight. Right here I learned that one must wash their head in the sea with clay. In Venice I had the opportunity of seeing all its sights and even of becoming very bored because I stayed there, contrary to my wishes, for about two weeks because of the following incident. Before I left Munich I shipped my suitcase through a forwarding agent to Venice, and this baggage arrived at the place perfectly in a week after my arrival—it arrived, but having lost its stamp in transit across the border between Bavaria and Austria, after which the forwarding agent supposedly could not have received it from the customs house, or more exactly could have, but only under the conditions of a payment to the customs house of 700 gulden, which he of course did not wish to do. According to him I could either wait while the matter of the loss of the stamp dragged on, or put the matter of receiving the baggage without the above in the hands of a lawyer. I do not know whether I hit upon a third method of action or who advised me, but instead of a lawyer I went to the Russian consul—I told him the whole story, and after several days I received a paper from him for the customs house, by which the suitcase was given to me.

From here I went nonstop to Florence. A great part of the way lay across what was at that time papal property (via Ferrara and Bologna), without a railway, and therefore I had to go in a coach, and in addition sit opposite an old Englishwoman, i.e., go almost the whole way cross-legged. Perhaps for this reason I have no pleasant memories about this trip. In Florence I met S. P. Botkin's brother, Pavel Petrovich, whom I knew a little in Moscow, and who was not at all like his brother. I must say a few words about him because he played an important role in one incident in Rome, which I will tell about below. He studied in the university in the department of law, but he was not an official and lived without business, enjoying his life now in Petersburg (with his artist brother), now in Moscow, staying with the family of a firm. Of a loose frame, a blond with a puffy, clean-shaven face, a soft, as if boneless, body and the same soft kind of manners, he was like a replete middle-aged Catholic priest, and he considered himself an old bachelor. He was a great lover of the theater, especially the ballet, and a still greater admirer of feminine beauty. He was thrilled and fell silent at the appearance of a beautiful woman's face, and if it was possible, expressed his sweet delights before the idol of the given moment by words, by his eyes, and by gestures. He was perhaps even a little carried away, but he was by nature a comedian and easily entered into his role and performed the comedy with great enthusiasm. I learned of this trait in his character later; I found out that among people who knew him intimately he made fun of his own delights. He ardently loved only himself and could not speak indifferently about misfortunes which had happened to him. Once in my presence he told Sergey Petrovich about his trip on the lakes of Finland, and when he began telling of a terrible moment, how on getting off a ship into a boat he stumbled and flew head first into the lake, his voice began to shake and tears came into his eyes. But instead of exclamations of sympathy, a laugh escaped Sergey Petrovich, who knew his brother's tendencies toward the comedian, and the rescued drowned man, not at all offended, finished his story with a description with a pathetic scene of how he came to, naked, under the hands of the sailors who were rubbing him and in a gust of gratitude began with tears kissing these Finns. I repeat again, I found out about this side of his character later, but then I considered him really capable of enthusiasm with a certain uncomely element.

Running around the streets of dear Florence (I appreciated the city in its real form later, on the third visit) and the city's art galleries continued for about three days, and then we set off together via Pisa for Livorno, and from here by ship to Civitavecchia and Rome. Pavel Petrovich had friends in Rome among the Russian artists, and he intended to stay there about two weeks or even longer. Therefore, probably on the first day of our arrival, he ran to the "Caffè Greco," at that time the place of gatherings of Russian artists, and probably thanks to one of them he rented for both of us two furnished rooms with a beautiful young Roman landlady. There, of course, I learned Al. Andr. Ivanov's address, visited him, and became acquainted with this fascinating, good old man with a pure, childlike soul. From the very first days evening teas were organized in our apartment, and Al. Andr. became a frequent guest for us. Not long before this he had become acquainted with Strauss' "Life of Christ" and was so carried away by the book that he decided to do a series of pictures from the life of the Saviour to this work. But first of all he considered it necessary to go to Strauss for advice and instructions for sources necessary for the artist. This journey was made (to some little town near Stuttgart where Strauss lived until our arrival in Rome), and Al. Andr. remained in general very pleased with it, although the discussions among the two old men were strained, according to Al. Andr.'s own words: the artist did not speak any other language than Italian, but Strauss did not understand Italian, and to be comprehensible to his discussion partner, spoke in Latin. Nevertheless, our old man obtained, according to Strauss' directions, several books, and among them one very important for him, in English (I do not remember the title) in which Solomon's temple from the time of Christ according to Josif Flavius was described. Having learned that I understood a little English, he persuasively asked me to look this book over and help him collate the readings concerning the dimensions of the walls and the internal structure of the temple with the facts of other sources from which he had already begun to draw a plan of the temple. I, of course, consented with joy, and the matter was arranged in the following way: several times a week I came to his room, read him the English book in Russian, and he, sitting behind the drawn plan with a pair of compasses in his hand, at one time collated the dimensions, at another entered what seemed to him as necessary in his notebook. If I had not broken off of myself during the readings to smoke and to say a few words concerning our business, then the old man probably would have let me read for hours without a breathing space—he was so carried away with the work, usually continuing right up to dinnertime. It is apropos to note here that Al. Andr.'s stomach was in great disorder because he did not take food well and often suffered with vomiting after dinner. He explained this—and absolutely seriously—not by a disorder of the stomach, but by the existence in Rome of un partito nemico (his own words), a hostile party which bribed tavern attendants where he dined to poison him. He suffered least of all (again his own words) from the redhaired waitress in the tavern Falcone, and therefore we almost always went for dinner in this establishment.

Before my mornings were arranged in such a way, Pavel Petrovich and I succeeded in visiting the most famous places in Rome and among other things, the chapel of the Holy Steps at the Lutheran cathedral. At the entrance to this chapel stood a monk who gave the zealous visitors directions concerning the method of honoring the holy things. The first to follow these directions was an old woman, and after her crept Pavel Petrovich himself, but not going halfway up the steps, he slipped back down. Then with a moved face and with a look of grief he gave the monk to understand through pantomime that he could not carry his zeal out to the end, and leaving the chapel he split his hides with laughter recalling the figure of the old woman creeping before him. Knowing only a few words in Italian, Pavel Petrovich was usually compelled in Italy to use pantomime, of which he was, like a ballet-lover, a great master, and with it, with an admixture of French words, he captivated our good landlady, Signora Maria.

Young, thin, well built, with the facial features of a Del Sarto Madonna, but lively and gay, she began to interest Pavel Petrovich from the very first brief meetings, much more than all the sights of Rome taken together; and he was able to conduct the matter in such a way that he very quickly subjected her to our society and to his civilities. The evening Russian teas which he arranged helped him very much in this respect. An enemy of any physical inconvenience (in Petersburg he kept a man-servant who not only dressed him from head to toe, but even brushed his hair), he prevailed upon Signora Maria to be hostess at these parties, pleading his own awkwardness and Russian customs. Together with this he paid his respects so deferentially that she agreed and came every day as a guest in the room which served as a salon for us. Several of these parties took place, and a trip to Tivoli was organized by the three of us together, i.e., with the landlady. We went there in a carriage which we had rented for the whole day; a light lunch upon arriving, then a ride on donkeys, a walk in the park, and the return back, when the heat had already abated. This trip, which was finished by a substantial dinner with wine, so affected Signora Maria that before we reached Rome she fell asleep in the carriage with a flushed face under the rays of the sun setting directly facing us. I do not believe that even artists could have dreamed of a more graceful sleeping beauty than our landlady during these moments. My roommate sat dumb from delight, and even I was very much touched, but in a way different from his, not at all a material way. This trip was a turntable in our mutual relations. He began to overdo in his attentions, and I began to be exasperated by his gushing glances and less and less ceremonious approaches. Little by little the matter came to a point where Signora Maria began, it seemed to me to be a poor, defenseless victim in the hands of a rich satyr. Her manner of reacting to his attentions misled me. As a very beautiful woman and as the landlady of our furnished rooms, she of course had to get used to the compliments of such a kind, and in my absence she probably answered them not with a jest, but in my presence, seeing that I regarded her differently, and probably noticing that Pavel Petrovich's compliments had an unpleasant effect on me, she did not know how she should answer them, awkwardly dismissed the matter with a joke, and from time to time even reddened and shrank back. But Pavel Petrovich, as I learned later from Sergey Petrovich, noticing that I was moved by our landlady and as if I was jealous of him over her, teased me with his compliments. How many times these irritating influences had an effect on me I do not remember, but they succeeded in bringing my nervous system to such a state that inevitably it ended in an outburst; and it came unexpectedly and nonsensically.

Before that memorable day when it happened, only Al. Andr. and some friend of Pavel Petrovich's from Petersburg, a deaf official, were guests at our evening teas; this particular time, not warning either me or the landlady, he brought about 5 people, Russian artists. Before they came, I was sitting in our salon with Signora Maria and I was talking with her in a most peaceful way; but when the guests appeared at the door of this room, she jumped up from her chair frightened, and I involuntarily after her; she began to hide behind my back, and I began to shield her from the looks of the dumbfounded company. Of course, this scene continued only a few seconds and concluded with Signora Maria's running out through the other doors to her room, and I, having lost my head and being very disconcerted, could hardly exchange greetings with the arrivals and immediately went to my room, seized my hat and went out of the house. The tea probably did not take place because when I returned after about two hours I found our apartment empty, locked myself in my room and gave myself over to meditations in which the question why Signora Maria was frightened was not broached (later I learned that one of the guests played some role in her past), but first and foremost appeared my idiotic behavior which had imparted to the scene which arose such an appearance as if we were caught on the spot of a crime—the behavior which had compromised a poor, defenseless girl. The fruit of these meditations was a letter written in which the guilty party in the scandal offered his hand and heart to the defenseless girl whom he had compromised. The next morning I found an opportunity to slip this letter into her hands and I ran away to Al. Andr. If I had told him the whole story this very day the matter could have taken a different turn, but I held my tongue, and in the evening of the same day I became the fiancé of the more astonished than gladdened fiancée, having made her promise to keep silent until a certain time. Soon after this Pavel Petrovich left, the ban was removed, and when I for my part told Al. Andr. that I intended to marry Signora Maria, he was grieved in a most sincere manner and he persuaded me to postpone the wedding until I had finished my studies abroad. To be a fiancé when you know that your fiancée is not marrying you for love, and moreover not to be able to speak to her well in her language was not very cheerful; but thank heavens she did not play the role of the happy fiancée; therefore our intimacy was limited to kissing only on parting, and even that took place without tenderness and without tears on either part. I left Rome at the end of October in a post carriage to Ancona, from here by steamship to Trieste and farther to cheerless Leipzig. Here I received several letters from Al. Andr. with some information concerning my fiancée; the ardor passed, and the whole story came to an end with my letter to the signora in which I informed her that I could not fulfill the promise I had made on account of the insurmountable resistance of my relatives. Thank goodness, according to Al. Andr.'s letters, I did not make her angry.

When I was in university in the last year I learned of the existence of Funke's textbook of physiology which came out at that time, and in Berlin I heard that Hoppe-Seyler was his comrade either in university or in the laboratory of Leman, then chairman of physiological chemistry, and this circumstance was the reason for my going to Leipzig for the 1857 winter semester. I called this city dismal, and at a nonfair time it was really this way, and besides the trip to Italy with the just described incident cost my generous pocket dearly, so that I had to lead a Spartan life here, and on top of it all without friends, in complete isolation. I remember the inexpensive Leipzig dinners: for 5 silbergroschen (15 kopeks) one could have a plate of soup, a half portion of meat with vegetables, and in the form of dessert "Hausbrod" (our rye bread), à discretion, with a lump of salted cottage cheese with caraway, also à discretion. I remember also my good apartment landlady, how at my request she substituted tea of a very strange odor for morning coffee because of an unwarranted addition of chicory to it, and to my question: why does the tea have such an aroma, she explained that she mixed clove into it for the odor.

Funke was an extraordinarius professor (the famous Ernst-Heinrich Weber was still the spokesman of the department, although he no longer lectured in physiology because of old age) and his laboratory, which consisted of two rooms, was arranged very poorly. I went there with a prepared topic—to study the influence of alcohol on nitrogen metabolism in the body, and on the muscles and nervous system. On the first of these problems I did experiments on myself, i.e., to measure on one and the same diet the daily discharges of urea and uric acid (at those times the said metabolism was measured namely in that way) under normal conditions and with use of alcohol. I fed myself in the next two weeks in the following way: in the morning and evening, identical portions of tea with dried crusts, and I dined in the student public house which I found near my apartment, which remained empty the whole day (in the evening no one was allowed there except the students of that party which rented it for the year), and the proprietor of which very willingly consented to give me daily a beefsteak of ¾ lean beef with a quantity of potatoes not varying in weight, and white bread.[1] On the second question I had to perform a great number of experiments first on a frog—on elasticity of the muscles, on the irritability of the muscles and the motor nerves, on the electrical properties of those and others, on the bandaging of vessels, and other things. From this aspect the studies were very useful, the more so as I was left to my own powers in the experiments. At that time, thanks to the methods of investigation worked out by Du Bois-Reymond and thanks to the recently done experiments of Claude Bernard and Kölliker, which had caused a lot of excitement, with the action of curare on nerves and muscles, experiments with the influence of various poisons on the muscle and nervous systems were very much in vogue, and I, at the same time while studying the influence of alcohol, repeated on the frog other experiments with the influence of various other poisons on the nerves and muscles. Meanwhile, Claude Bernard's experiments with the action of sulphurcyanic potassium came to my attention, and repeating the experiments, I found an error in them. The matter was that the different aspects of electrical stimulation of nerves and muscles had not yet at that time come from Germany to the laboratory at Paris, and Bernard still used pince'electrique—compasses with copper and zinc ends—for stimulation of them. Thus a description in German of my own experiments with the correction of the mistake which I had noticed became my first very simple scientific work to be awarded with publication. In Leipzig I had the honor of being introduced for the first time into good German society, namely to the evening gathering of a certain group, the members of which were, among other people, professors with their families. Funke took me with him to one of these gatherings, obliging me to wear a tail coat and have white gloves.

---

[1] At these dinners I learned from the proprietor, who was very friendly about these evening visits, how they passed time in the public house, and meanwhile I heard stories about a certain student, Motz, who on a bet drank 32 glasses of beer during the course of an evening (from 6 to 12 o'clock).

The meeting would begin with a short lecture or a story, the contents of which were popular and pleasant to the ladies. This time it was Funke's turn to entertain them with a lecture, and he satisfied the public very much by telling what the difference was between Nahrungs und Genussmitteln.[2] Just when the signal was given to those for the quadrille to begin, he presented me to some young lady, having said beforehand how to invite her for the quadrille, and found us facing each other. The quadrille went well. Before the waltz he introduced me to another lady, and going around with her for some time, I brought her, according to the Russian custom, to the chair from which I had taken her, bowed, and began to move away, but was caught by Funke's laugh, who said that by their customs, while the music continues to play a dance the man does not have the right to leave the lady he has chosen and must dance with her continually, or at least sit near her and converse.

For Christmas I went to Berlin to my dear friends and very joyously met them in 1858. On New Year's Eve the theatrical hall in Krolle's establishment was turned into a huge restaurant hall with many separate tables at which we feasted, side by side with the familyless youth and family circles. Thanks to the latter circumstance, ladies could be present also at the tables of those without families. It was very gay and passed without scandal. It was so miserable returning from Berlin to Leipzig that I inwardly decided not to hold out to the end of the semester, and when I received the news from one of my friends that there was a vacancy in Hoppe's laboratory and that he would take me, I returned I think at the end of February to his fine laboratory. Having the object of finishing as a dissertation the influence of alcohol on the function of the liver, I considered it necessary to become a skilled hand at quantitative analysis of bile for its component parts, and began to study this question. At that time I probably studied an extract of glycogen from the liver. Botkin was not in Berlin at this time; I think he was temporarily in Moscow and I was ill there with the first attacks of bilious colic. I still remember this short interval of time because being shortwinded all of a sudden, once I so badly frighted good, stout frau Krüger, the landlady of Botkin's apartment where I visited, that she brought the district doctor to me, whom I had to pay 20 silbergroschen for the visit and prescription, in which he intended for me to recover by using raspberry syrup acidified with phosphoric acid—and I got well.

I do not know whether some good person advised me or whether I in my own mind came to the decision of going from here to Vienna to Ludwig, but in the spring of 1858 I was already with this incomparable teacher, who was famous at this time for his skill in vivisection as well as important work on circulation of the blood and sections, and later became an international teacher of physiology for almost all parts of the world. To occupy such a position, there

[2] Food and flavoring substances.

was little of certain talent (Helmholtz, while he was a physiologist, and Du Bois-Reymond, in all his long activity, had few laboratory students); besides talent and variety of knowledge, certain traits of character were still necessary in a teacher, and also methods of teaching which would make a period in the laboratory not only a useful, but a pleasant business for the student. Invariably friendly, cheerful and gay both in moments of rest and at work, he took a direct part in everything which was undertaken according to his instructions, and usually worked not by himself, but together with the students, carrying out with his own hands for them the hardest parts of the problem and only now and then printing his own name beside the student's name who worked more than half by the teacher's hands. However, while Ludwig lived in Vienna, serving as a professor in a small military-medical school (Josephinum), there was no place for him to display these qualities widely. His laboratory consisted of three rooms: a very small library (his study), an auditorium for about 50 people, and the so-called workshop where laboratory attendant Salfenmozer, the professor's right hand, of course well known to all of Ludwig's students, worked. I must add to this that the school was a closed institution; the laboratory according to the regulations was not intended for the student's practical studies, and the professor did not receive a fee from the students. For all these reasons during the whole year of my stay only two of us worked there in the laboratory (in the beginning, Wilhelm Müller and I, then Max Germann and I, both of my co-workers extremely nice people), and did not pay a kopek for the right to work.

I came to Ludwig without a recommendation and was the first Muscovite that he saw (later he could distinguish three types among Russians, by name Petersburgites, Muscovites, and Little Russians). Talking with me about my intention to study the influence of alcohol on the circulation of the blood and absorption of oxygen by the blood, he made a kind of examination for me on physiology, and probably satisfied himself with respect to the answers because he let me in the laboratory. I received a place in the workshop, where all of his Viennese students in general worked, and Salfenmozer was instructed to help me in my experiments.

While I dawdled with the absorption of alcohol by the blood and kymograph curves of a normal and intoxicated animal—the whole summer semester went for this because of my inexperience at that time—Ludwig did not take any part in the fate of my experiments, only asking me from time to time whether everything was going well for me, knowing of course from Salfenmozer that in outward form the experiments were going without detraction. Ludwig of course, could not become interested in them, and perhaps he was sizing up the Muscovite. His only attention toward me was expressed in the following way: on those mornings when he did not work with W. Müller[3] and himself con-

---

[3] These experiments consisted of a study of breathing phenomena under conditions when

tinued his own experiments with innervation of a salivary gland, I was invited
to assist him in these experiments. They consisted of a graphic representation
of acts of secreting saliva registered on the surface of a revolving drum in the
form of descending curves. With this aim, the small vessel into which the
saliva of the submaxillary gland flowed was supplied with a writing point,
and being suspended on an extremely weak spring (i.e., a very tensile one), it
went down between two guide bars without friction, continuously down according to the degree of filling by saliva. For me, these experiments were not only
interesting and instructive but also entertaining because the professor, at that
time essentially still a young man of 40 years, loved to chatter at his work:
he told gay anecdotes from old university life about crank-professors, questioned me about Russia, knew the name of Ulybyshev (it seems so), in his
words, as the best critic of Beethoven's music; he was interested in Lermontov,
knew him probably by the German translations and once even wanted to hear
how his verses sounded in Russian, to which I recited for him *The Gifts of
Terek* with a translation of their thought. When V. Müller left, I alone remained with him, he took me even closer to himself, inviting me to assist and
be present at all his experiments which were prepared for his lectures. He, of
course, would have let me come to his lectures for the students, but I did not
have a right to this.

I must say that this was a very happy time for me. I did not have any
Russian friends this semester, but I was not deprived of company. For discussions in the laboratory there was V. Müller (later a professor of pathological
anatomy at Jena), a Bavarian, student from Erlanger, in love with his country
and its beer, satisfied with everything and complaining only about the expen-
siveness of life in Vienna. Once, to my wonder regarding this and in answer
to my story about the low cost of Leipzig meals he, not without bragging, remarked: "What kind of cheapness is this! In Erlanger we students could
dine for much less and were full, getting a plate of soup and a klyotska."[4]
Being acquainted with this name in Russia, by soup and klyotskas I of course
did not understand how one klyotska could satiate a student who was not generally noted for a poor appetite, and understood the enigma only when Müller
demonstrated for me with both hands its size, in the shape of a ball, almost as
big as a human head. I stayed in the laboratory with V. Müller for two months,
and then we did not meet any more in life; but I lived in Vienna a whole year
with my other friend of this time, formed a friendship with him to such a
degree that I was guest for months in his laboratory when we were both pro-

---

the lung cavity of an animal, on which a tracheotomy had been performed, communicated
with a very small O_2 receiver in the form of a bell immersed in mercury. Its level served
as a measure of the animal's use of gas from it. It turned out that when all the gas
disappeared from under the bell, all the oxygen disappeared from the air in the lungs,
not leaving a single trace.

[4] A klyotska is a kind of dumpling.

fessors (he in Harz and I in Petersburg), and I preserve a feeling of friendship toward him even now. Thank goodness he is still living and has become
for me the only friend of my youth, whereas all my friends whom I have
described in these cursory lines, and even all my dear German teachers have
long ago departed from this life.

Rollet, assistant to Brücke, professor of physiology at the University of
Vienna, became my friend. A that time he was studying the solution of blood
corpuscles by electrical discharges through blood, and he came to Ludwig's
laboratory to show him the results he had obtained. I became acquainted with
him here, and then we began to dine every day at one and the same time in the
same small restaurant on Alserstrasse. Being utterly devoted to his own affair,
he mainly discussed scientific problems, and not at all wishing to lecture, he
imparted to me much that was interesting from what happened in Brücke's
laboratory in the line of physiological chemistry and histology. He spoke
slowly, as if thinking over each word, and all his actions were notable for the
same deliberation. An enemy of any hypocrisy, and at the same time direct
and sincere to the point of naïveté, he, in the most serious way in conversations, corrected my errors in articulation of German and experienced errors
in physiology. Calm and even a little phlegmatic in appearance, he was, however,
sharply animated, sharing any event which took place in science or in life; he
regarded the clericals harshly, as enemies of any progress and enemies of
Austria. He was indifferent towards women, he did not like Viennese women,
calling them shallow coquettes, greedy for luxury. In general he belonged to
that class of people with warm hearts with incongruously calm exteriors. It
was enough to see once on his plain face a nice smile to know that this was a
very good man.

I stayed in Vienna for the fall holidays in 1858 to write my dissertation,
since I had finished collecting my experimental material, and here I had the
opportunity of enlarging upon the literary data which I had already gathered
on the problem. Walks about the closest environs, open air Strauss concerts
in Volksgarten, and a trip by steamship along the Danube to Lentz and back,
were my only amusement. This part of the Danube seemed less beautiful to
me than the banks of our Volga in the Kostroma province.

In the fall Bekkers and Botkin came to Vienna for the winter semester, the
latter a fiancé after a trip to Moscow. His wedding was to be performed in
Vienna in the spring of the following year when he had completed the winter
semester, for which the bride had to come to Vienna with her mother. Thus,
here also, as in Berlin, were three young friends working the greater part of the
day and having a good time during hours of rest. Vienna, of course, was live-
lier than Berlin, but we enjoyed ourselves much more modestly here than there.
Thus, of all the entertainment places we visited I remember, by the sharp difference of impressions, two balls of perfectly decorous form; a ball of German

burghers and a ball of Slavs, at another time, but in one and the same locale. At the first of these that degree of animation reigned in the dancing hall which was inherent in balls of good society in Russia, also, but especially since, besides the usual all-European dances, here was first and foremost a beautiful Viennese waltz which I saw for the first time then, with its slow tempo and beautiful swinging of the body from side to side—a dance undoubtedly beautiful but calm and more lulling than captivating. We went to the Slavic ball with greater interest since in the announcements it was stated that there would be national dances in accordance with the desire. This time, after an insipid quadrille, waltz and polkas, only two national dances were formed: a boring Serbian kolo like our round dance, only without the refrain "along the sea," and a mazurka of real Poles. In my life I never saw a more captivating dance: our ballet mazurka in "Life for the Tsar," with Kshesinskiy in the first couple is a miserable parody on this fiery dance. The couples floated about the hall like a whirlwind, and the Poles did not dance, but ran as if to the music, and they ran flushing, agitated, panting. At the burghers' ball, in the restaurant adjacent to the dancing hall there was a lot of noise, loud conversations, the ring of dishes, but no shrieks at all, nor toasts, nor jumping up from the chairs—in a word, no signs of a tipsy party. But at the Slavs', in the very same room, there was an abundance: at one table they were talking with shouts of bravo, at another they were kissing; here they suppressed a speaker who had jumped up from his chair by pulling him to the floor, and there was heard booming laughter or the knocking on the table with a fist. In a word, there was a sumptuous feast.

At the very beginning of this semester Botkin and Bekkers, having made arrangements with other Russian medical students who had come to Vienna, commissioned me to ask Ludwig if he would not give a series of lectures in his laboratory on the circulation of the blood and the innervation of the blood vessels. I carried out their wish, and Ludwig agreed to do it if a sum of three hundred gulden was collected among those who wanted it. Of course the sum was collected, and I was among those who attended these lectures. Ludwig belonged to that group of professors who like the procedure of reading, and at their lectures act as if they relish what they are reading. From the vivisection side, the lectures were splendidly arranged and were of course very successful. When the lectures were finished the grateful participants invited the professor to a dinner arranged in his honor, and he accepted the invitation. Here he behaved as a comrade with us, was gay, conversed, became a little tipsy, and after dinner played billiards with me. At dinner he became acquainted with both of my friends, and later becoming acquainted with S. P. Botkin's charming wife, he was very well disposed toward this pair. How pleasant he was with us can be shown by the following minor incident. Bekkers sometimes visited me in the laboratory to make arrangements concerning some evening business, and once he came at a time when Ludwig sat fixing a comparatively thick cannula in a thin lymphatic vessel. Seeing Bekkers and knowing that he was a surgeon, he met him with the words: "Here you've come just in time, if you please, Mr. Pirogov, sit in my place and put this piece in the lymphatic vessel for me. I'm struggling with it here and can't get it in." Bekkers sat down, and as luck would have it, he got it in. On Ludwig's part this was of course a joke directed to the young man whom he liked.

This same winter my work in the laboratory took a good turn.

The experiments of adding alcohol vapor to blood freed from gases with the purpose of studying its influence on the absorption of O_2 by the blood had given me unsatisfactory results during the past semester; therefore, I began to think that it might have been more rational to proceed otherwise: to single out from the blood of a normal and an intoxicated animal the gases contained in it and compare these values with each other. Having read a description of the then existing methods of Magnus and L. Meyer, I could not but see that both of these were unsatisfactory—in one the blood boils at room temperature, and in the other in the unreplaced empty space, because during the whole winter semester I had pumped the gases from the blood by the continuous action of an air pump and had at the same time to heat it to 38-40° C.

FIG. 1

to free it of gases. Whether I meditated on how to get out of this difficulty for a long time I do not know, but in the end the thought came to me to use the absorptiometer of L. Meyer and convert it by small changes to a blood pump with replaced vacuum and the possibility of heating the blood. No sooner said than done (see the supplementary schematic drawing). To the arc *di* of the absorptiometer *abdi* was soldered tube *f* (the only glass at that time in Vienna with an old bore still working on an oil lamp!), joining with tube *g* by rubber, the long glass tube *h* fastened onto the vent tube *c*; finally, tube *ab* was cut on its lower part and both pieces were joined with rubber. The experiment with such an apparatus was carried out in the following way: first of all the receptacle *e* with the rubber section and its clamp, *i*, was filled with the blood of the animal, not in contact with air, for which it was filled to the top with mercury, tipped over into a mercury bath, and under its lower end was placed a tube through which flowed the blood from the blood vessels of the animal. Then, at the blocked clamp *i* the receptacle was shaken, the blood let into it was defibrinated with the mercury remaining in it, and the receptacle was fastened to the free end of arc *di*. After this, at the blocked clamp *l* the whole apparatus was filled with mercury, the lower end of tube *h* was submerged in mercury, clamps *m*, *n*, *p* were blocked, and clamp *l* was opened. If the length of tube *h* is such that the distance between points *q* and *l* exceeds the height of the barometer, then letting mercury through *l* into the space *ifdg* forms a vacuum. Then open clamp *i*, and the warm blood which is rushing with force into the empty space pushes the mercury left in arc *di* out. The gases isolated from the blood are transferred very easily to tube *g* if, having closed clamp *p* and squeezed the gases a little, one then opens clamp *m*.

In place of the gas entering tube *g*, from it there always flows a corresponding volume of mercury into the space *ifdg*, meaning, the operation of letting the mercury through *l* and the boiling of the blood in a vacuum can be repeated and is repeated the desired number of times until the boiling stops giving off gas into the vacuum.

Ludwig of course saw these test experiments, and they served as a model for the blood pump that he immediately ordered, which was put at my disposal and which I described in my following work with the gases of arterial blood of a normal and an asphyxiated animal. By this method, studies about the gases of the blood were placed on firm footing, and these very experiments, as well as the long fussing with L. Meyer's absorptiometer, were the reason that I devoted a very significant part of my life to problems about the blood's gases and about the absorption of gases by liquids.

This winter I was received in Ludwig's family, which consisted of his wife, a very modest, taciturn woman, and a daughter of 15. Once I was even in a tail coat at an evening party, where the public sat around a table, the sedate ladies on a sofa, and Ludwig's daughter carried tea to the guests, and where among the guests was the Viennese astronomist (I think Littrow) with his grown daughter, probably a very educated girl who questioned me about Russia. From this time my dear teacher's friendly disposition toward me did not cease, right up to his death, manifesting itself at all the little turns in my life with warm, compassionate letters.

Botkin's wedding was to take place, as I have said, at the end of the winter semester, and the time of his fiancée's arrival was drawing so near that he had already begun to collect some adornments for his wife's future boudoir (I remember the laughably short mirror which he built, adorned with towels, which probably made his refined fiancée laugh) and we had new tail coats made since I had to be best man at the wedding, when suddenly one beautiful morning poor Botkin woke up with a rash which fortunately turned out to be chicken pox. It is clear that this strongly affected the mood of the always cheerful and good Botkin (by this incident it seems even the coming of his fiancée was postponed); and at this ill-starred time we had the misfortune of starting an argument about the essence of life phenomena. . . . Under other conditions the argument could have ended rationally, with amendments and concessions on one and another side, but in this case these did not follow, and it finished on

Botkin's side with a proverb just for that time: "He who confuses the end and the beginning has bast in the head," which hurt my feelings so much that we did not see each other any more in Vienna, and I left for Heidelberg.

I am quoting in word for word a very important excerpt from Ludwig's letter to me of May 4, 1859, that is, in the beginning of my stay in Heidelberg.

"Dear Sechenov, Botkin left, married, and will have, of course, a pleasant and happy honeymoon. In one of our private meetings he reported to me that he had received a letter from Mr. Glebov (Herr Kleboff), a certain high-ranking official in Petersburg, in which he says that if you (i.e., I, Sechenov) wrote to him how and where you studied physiology, he, having such a document in his hands, could intercede for you. Carry this out. I asked Botkin to write you about this himself, and I hope that he will do this since his wife tried very hard to persuade him (eifrig zuredete). As she complained about Botkin's unwarranted touchiness, so he complained about yours. Forgive me for talking about this, but I have wanted so much to establish an agreement between two people each of whom in his own way could do much good (jeder in seiner Art soviel Gutes wirken kann). Give my heartfelt regards to Bunsen and Helmholtz. Yours truly, K. Ludwig."

I do not remember when I wrote the letter to Glebov, but I know that several days after I received Ludwig's letter I met happy, good Botkin and his beautiful wife in Heidelberg. This happened apparently on some holiday because they, accompanied by Yunge (who was with me in Heidelberg), who knew where I went to walk, found me in the park near the castle. Since this time I have never argued with Sergey Petrovich about cellules and molecules . . .

I came to Heidelberg with the intention of attending the lectures of Helmholtz and Bunsen and working in both laboratories. Knowing that they did not study organic chemistry at Bunsen's, I announced my desire to study titration and analysis of gases. Knowing that I was a medical student, he suggested that I first of all study alkalimetry and analysis of mixtures of atmospheric air with CO_2. Hearing of Bunsen's perfect goodness and simplicity, I talked to him without being embarrassed, but to Helmholtz, then already a great physiologist in the eyes of the whole world, I went with trepidation, carrying in my head the whole layout of the conversation. I came to him with the following four plans of work: 1) to study the influence on the heart of simultaneous stimulation of both vagi, one in a centrifugal, and the other in a centripetal direction; 2) to study by means of his, i.e., Helmholtz's, myograph the different contraction speeds of various muscles of the frog, citing as an example the great difference in the movements of the front and back extremities of male frogs; 3) to study under his direction some problem from physiological optics; and 4) to allow me to do several experiments with the extraction of gases from milk by means of the blood pump just built by Ludwig, which I would furnish (on coming to Heidelberg I immediately ordered it on my own account from the mechanic Dezaga). I did not receive any answer on the first point, probably because no vivisections were done in his laboratory except on frogs; on the second point, Helmholtz expressed his approval, saying that at the present time they were already working with this instrument; he promised to give me a topic, and allowed me to do the experiments with milk.

What can I say about this outstanding man? By the insignificance of my education I could not draw near to him, since I saw him, so to speak, only from a distance, and besides, always remained quiet in his presence, which hampered him himself. From his quiet figure with thoughtful eyes breathed a certain peace, as if he were not from this world. However strange this is, I speak the real truth: he produced on me an impression like that which I experienced on seeing for the first time the Sikstin Madonna in Dresden, the more so because his eyes, by their expression, were indeed like the eyes of this Madonna. He probably produced the same impression also on his near acquaintances. Much later, when he was in Berlin, according to rumors, he was very often invited by Wilhelm I, who acted as if he liked to converse with him. On a trip through Leipzig I asked Ludwig what could interest a military man—Wilhelm I—in Helmholtz? To this Ludwig answered in a certain especially tender voice: es ist doch ein Genu ein so ruhiges Denken zu hören dwieas seinige ist.[5] In Germany they considered him a national treasure and were very displeased with the description by a certain Englishman that in appearance Helmholtz was more like an Italian than a German.

He lectured plainly at his regular lectures to the medical students, which I heard, and which were given in an elementary way without any mathematics. I was probably bored because I once had had the occasion to be at an evening meeting of a Heidelberg scholarly society at which he described his analysis of sounds by resonators, and he lectured here even gaily, picking out as a judge the deaf Bunsen, who was present at this report, and who smiled a good smile when Helmholtz placed the resonator in his ear.

Four people: two ophthalmologists—Yunge (my friend) and Knap, a German with very squinted eyes whose name I do not remember (and who spent several months with Helmholtz' myograph), and myself, worked in the laboratory (very small, with the professor's separate room and without the separate room of his assistant at that time, Bundt). Bundt sat the whole year unfailingly at some books in his own corner, not paying any attention to anyone and not saying a word to anyone. I did not once hear his voice. We would catch only a glimpse of Helmholtz. Every day he passed once into the work room, made the rounds of all those working, asked each one if everything was going all right, and gave explanations if they were needed.

I began to work on the topic Helmholtz gave me; but before he gave it to me

[5] It is always a delight to listen to such peaceful thoughts as his are.

he asked me whether I knew English, and with my affirmative answer he let me read Stokes' treatise on fluorescence. The topic consisted of a determination of the relaxation of the transparent media of the eye to ultraviolet rays. Earlier, he himself had ascertained the fluorescence of the retina in these ways. We had quartz lenses and prisms in the laboratory, but there was not yet the silver mirror (for heliostat) which they had begun to prepare by Liebig's method not long before that, and Helmholtz, knowing that I worked with Bunsen, told me that I could make it in Bunsen's laboratory. Probably he himself told Bunsen about this because I had hardly mentioned this when Bunsen grabbed with his hands a glass plate, cleaned it, silvered it, and in the end polished it with a velvet cushion. I obtained pig eyes from a slaughter house, and as soon as I set a path of light from the heliostat across the work room and a little window in the wall of the auditorium, from the very first experiments I came across an intense blue fluorescence of the crystalline lens in ultraviolet rays. When I showed this phenomenon to Helmholtz he, in the place of the pig eye, placing my own in the path of the light, found that my crystalline lens was also fluorescent, and immediately noticed that this was a very convenient method of demonstrating the close contiguity of the pupil to the anterior surface of the crystalline lens, i.e., the absence of the so-called posterior chamber of the eye. The letter I received on this occasion from Ludwig made me very happy; I probably wrote to him that I did not feel so free and welcome in Heidelberg as with him in Vienna. Here are excerpts from this letter: ". . . Helmholtz hat an Brücke geschrieben, dass Sie eine beträchtliche Fluorescenz der Linse entdeckt haben . . . Und dann ist der Umgang mit H. doch höchst lehrreich, im nächsten Winter werden sich vielleicht die Berührungspunkte zwischen ihm und ihnen mehren; schon jetzt schreibt er mir, dass sie ihm gut gefallen."[6]

This letter was of June 29, 1859. It meant that the whole winter semester went for studies at Bunsen's and for this work. When this work was written up and presented to Helmholtz, he found the following invention of mine in it; does not the blue fluorescence of the crystalline lens play a role in our seeing the air as blue. He remarked on this invention: if this was so, then we could not see distinctly the ultraviolet part of the spectrum with his Fraungofer lens because the fluorescence gives diffused light; and in such a way the invention was withdrawn from application.

Bunsen lectured excellently, and had the unconquerable habit at lectures of smelling the odorous substances described, however harmful and bad the odors were. They recounted how once he smelled something until he fainted. Long ago he had paid for his weakness for explosive substances with his eye,

[6] Helmholtz wrote to Brücke: you [Sechenov] discovered the considerable fluorescence of the crystalline lens . . . and now contact with H. is instructive in the highest degree; perhaps next winter the points of contact between you and him will multiply; and he writes me now that he likes you very much.

but at any opportunity in his lectures he produced explosions. Like this even now, he would blow up iodine-nitrogen and chlorine nitrogen in open leaden crucibles arming himself with a long stick with a pen stuck into its end at right angles, and wearing glasses, and then he solemnly showed us drops of the latter combination on the bottom punctured by the explosion. Suffering from forgetfulness, he often appeared at a lecture with a twisted ear—a heritage of school age preserved to old age.[7] When during the lecture the helix settled into shape (became normal) by a movement of the professor's hand this meant that the memorandum had done its part—the crucial point was not forgotten. And when, as it not infrequently happened, the ear remained twisted, at the end of the lecture the students dispersed with gay conversations about whether the crucial point outlined was forgotten or the ear forgotten. Bunsen was a general favorite, and they called him none other than Papa Bunsen, although he was not yet an old man.

In Heidelberg, immediately on arriving, I found a large Russian company: the T. P. Passek family (mother and three sons) from Moscow, known to me; the chemist Savich, who studied with Erlenmeyer; three young people who did not leave any trace by themselves; and in direct contrast to them in this respect—Dmitriy Ivanovich Mendeleyev. Later—I think in the winter—A. P. Borodin came. Mendeleyev, of course, became the head of our group, all the more so as, despite his young years (he was younger than I), he was already a prepared chemist, and we were students. In Heidelberg he brought gas at his own expense to one of the rooms at our apartment, acquired a chemical dish, and with a cathetometer from Salleron he sat down to the study of capillary phenomena, not visiting anyone's laboratories. T. P. Passek frequently invited Dmitriy Ivanovich and myself to her place now for tea, now for Russian pie or Russian cabbage soup, and among her family we always met Mrs. Marko-Vovchok, a teacher, who was introduced to her face as such, but behind her back as a poor woman, suffering from her husband's strict temper. Whether she did not pay any attention to us or we did not grow to an understanding of the heart-felt treasures contained in her, I, at least, do not retain in my memory any impressions of her in this direction—no more than that she was a blond, not beautiful, but a very young and rather heavy woman, without any signs of torment on her face.

This summer, and the winter following it, our life flowed so quietly and monotonously that summer and winter impressions are mixed up in my mind and I remember only separate minor episodes. I remember, for example, that in the apartment of Mendeleyev *The Precipice* by Goncharov was loudly read; it had just come out at that time, and the audience listened to it greedily, and

[7] As far as I remember, our students did not study this operation on the ear, which consisted of pushing from behind on the helix forcing it forward.

with our hunger it seemed to us the height of perfection. I remember that
A. P. Borodin, who had a piano in his apartment sometimes entertained an
audience with music, carefully concealed the fact that he was a serious musician because he never played anything serious, but only certain songs or
favorite arias from Italian operas, on request from his audience. Thus learning that I passionately loved *The Barber of Seville*, he treated me to all the
principal arias of this opera, and generally astonished us all very much by
being able to play anything that we asked, without notes, by memory. I
remember, finally, a certain very amusing incident. It probably happened in
the summer because a salon car served as the scene of the action, and these
cars left Heidelberg only in the summer. Going to Mannheim to the theater,
our company of 6 people (Savich and Mendeleyev were among us) got into a
salon car first and took a table in the corner farthest from the door of the car.
After several minutes in the same car Professor Friedrich seated some lady at
the very entrance and himself went away. At this moment Dmitriy Ivanovich
had just begun to roll a cigarette, but catching sight of the woman, he stopped
halfway, and holding the yet unrolled paper with the tobacco in his hand, he
turned to the woman with the question whether she would permit smoking.
He did not have the first words out when the lady jumped up from her place
in fright and ran outside. Neither she nor Professor Friedrich appeared
again, and we with great chagrin understood that by a misunderstanding on
the lady's part a scandal came about in which they would accuse us Russians
of rudeness and ignorance. Fortunately, Professor Friedrich personally knew
Savich, who was receiving treatment from him, and we entrusted Savich
immediately on arriving in Mannheim to find Professor Friedrich and tell him
what happened. In Savich's words, Friedrich during the first minute turned
his back on him, not saying a word, but when he had heard the story, he split
his sides with laughter, saying that his wife imagined that we were inviting
her to play cards.

In Heidelberg I became acquainted with Boris Nikolayevich Chicherin. He
did not join Mendeleyev's company, and was seen from time to time only with
Yunge and with me, as his school fellows in the university. He was already a
junior scientific assistant.

In the fall holidays in 1859 Dmitriy Ivanovich and I set off together for
Switzerland to have a good time, having in mind to do everything prescribed
for real lovers of Switzerland, i.e., to climb Rigi, to spend the night in the
hotel, to feast our eyes upon the "Alpengrühen" to go for a ride on Vierwald-
stätter lake to Flüel, and to go on foot over the whole Oberland. We carried
this program out exactly, and we even spent two days in Interlaken, waiting
in vain for the beauty of Ingfrau to unwrap itself from the fog which covered
it. But what I did with myself then I positively do not remember.

In the beginning of the winter semester which followed this, Ludwig's pump which I had ordered was ready, and I set to work on the gases of milk. With this aim I had to hire from a Heidelberg druggist, upon deposit of its value, the required quantity of mercury, and entered, after long persuasion, into the following agreement with a petty bourgeois of the town of Heidelberg who had cow's milk for sale. At a very early hour of the morning before she milked the cow I came to her with a big laboratory cup, a bottle of olive oil and a glass container for the milk, filled beforehand with mercury. The cup was filled with the oil, and the proprietress had to milk the cow dipping the teats in the oil. After this the container was closed with a clamp, was tipped over into the milk, the clamp opened, and the milk of course rose to the top, and the mercury flowing out was concealed in the milk's film. When the owner of the cow saw this spectacle for the first time she was half very astonished, and half frightened, and clasped her hands and almost ran away—she raised the container with the mercury behind the silver bottle with opaque sides and suddenly saw that the milk ran up along the side and collected there, not running down. I explained to her with difficulty that it was not sorcery. Helmholtz saw my experiments with the milk and Ludwig's pump, of course, since they took place in his laboratory and, after six years, there was first described in Wundt's textbook an incomparably handier form of pump constructed by Helmholtz (two unequal sizes of vessel communicating with each other by a long non-collapsible rubber hose), which is still present in pumps with a Torricelli vacuum. Not knowing about this, I also described in 1865 a very simple form of pump. Here the Torricelli vacuum was formed by the action of the usual air pump. The history of these three forms can be found in "Scheidlen's physiol. Methodik, 3-te Liefer, 1877."

The only event this winter which disturbed the usual quiet life of Heidelberg was the celebration of Schiller's centennial. Our group always dined in the Badischer Hof Hotel restaurant and ate at one end of a long table; at the other end sat students—Prussian barons who walked about town in white hats with whips in their hands and with Great Danes. On the anniversary day, at dinner among the barons sat the gray Mittermeyer (a professor of the law faculty), who made a speech recalling that in early youth he had the good fortune to see the great man, describing his education, humanity, breadth of views, and concluding his speech with Schiller's views on women, describing the feminine types in his works. During the evening we attended a theatrical performance of "The Wallenstein Camps" (to tell the truth, it was very boring) which finished with an apotheosis.

My studies in the laboratory ended with my experiments with milk. My finances came to an end and I would have had to return to Russia right away if I had not received a small inheritance of 500 rubles in December. With this wealth in my pocket I set off with Mendeleyev and Borodin for Paris. Several days before this trip, a whitlow grew on my hand, one so bad that with sleepless nights it aroused the compassion, even of our circle, in a certain Russian society lady (I was not acquainted with her and she found out about my ailment from one of those young Russians who did not leave any traces after themselves). She advised me to put sour cream with down on the finger. I did not do this, but went to Paris with a little fever in Savich's raccoon coat so that I would not catch cold on the way. We left on Christmas Eve and, passing Strasbourg at night from the bridge to the railway station, we much admired the continuous sea of Christmas tree lights. In those times, the German railway along which we had to travel went only to Kehl; here the passengers changed to a coach (the baggage was sent separately and passed by customs in Paris), crossed the Rhine bridge, and stopped at the French gates to have our passports checked, the passenger remaining in the coach. Having returned our passports, the French official began to call our names. The first two, Mendeleyev and Borodin, came out all right, but he hesitated over my name and, looking at my dark figure in an unusual suit, he could not hold out from the question, "Are you a Turk, Sir?" This brightened up the whole company, including himself.

Never in all my life have I had such a good time as I did in Paris. For the first week or more I was nowhere but in establishments like today's "Closerie de lilas" (a student dance class) where there was a commotion, in theaters with suppers after performances and, of course, I was at the Bol'shoy Opera's masquerade ball, with confetti in my pocket for treating the dancers, Spanish girls, bayaderes, etc. It finally came to my calming down and beginning to feel sick when not even half of the wealth I had brought remained in my pocket. At that time, Bekkers taught in Paris, and having already become acquainted with the vain side of Parisian life, he did not take part in my diversions. He introduced me to one of my future friends at the medical academy and his kind, amiable, intelligent wife, at whose place gathered the Petersburg students in Paris. He himself took me to lectures of the then professor of theoretical surgery (Malgaigne), which were interspersed with anecdotes told with French stylishness. At one of his lectures, for example, I heard reminiscences from the distant past, such as: "From the times when I fought with Emperor Nikolay . . .," referring to the time of the Polish uprising. At the next lecture he cited to his audience a lengthy list of doctors, doctors' assistants, and druggists who took part in the operation on Louis XIV's rectal fistula, with a detailed account of how much they received for it —a grand total of 70,000 francs. For this lecture a then famous master of surgical instruments (I do not remember his name) brought him his own écraseur and was very disturbed when the professor, having described the use of the instrument, said that it perhaps would come in handy in very few cases, but it was of no use at all where it was possible to manage with a knife. Botkin was also in Paris. Just before our arrival in December, twins were born to him. In taking care of his wife and the newborn children, he did not show himself anywhere, and I only caught a glimpse of him.

Soon, on returning from Paris, I had to get everything ready for the way back. I did not want to return to my native country because for three and one-half years I was used to a life of freedom, without obligations, and study of great interest. Besides, one could not help loving the Germany of that time with its simple, good, open-hearted inhabitants (in a vast majority). The Germany of that time presents itself to me even now in the form of fulfilled peace and the quiet of a landscape at the time when the lilac, apple trees and cherry trees bloom, showing as white spots against the green background of the clearings cut up by vistas of poplars. Be that as it may, I had to go when I had remaining in my pocket just enough money for a stopover in Berlin and for the trip from there to Petersburg. Helmholtz said goodbye to me affectionately and entrusted to me three reprints of his work (which later made up one of the chapters of his famous book about sound sensations) with a request to give them to Magnus, Dovey and Du Bois-Reymond in Berlin, which I of course did. On this occasion, Du Bois-Reymond met me affably and, having wished me future success, remarked that I had already been in all the places where I ought to have been.

6

RETURN TO RUSSIA
AND PROFESSORSHIP AT THE
PETERSBURG MEDICAL ACADEMY
(1860-1870)

THE WINTER route lay by railroad to Königsberg and from there through Tauroggen to Riga to Petersburg by post carriage. In Königsberg I got a place in the back four-seat compartment with three ladies, a French modiste who was returning from Paris to Petersburg, a girl from Riga who spoke French fluently, and a very young German girl who was going somewhere not far from Königsberg. Whether, from not being used to a trip in a closed spring carriage, or because we were sitting on the front seat and were riding with our backs forward, the poor German girl began to pale with obvious signs of nausea, but only during the very beginning of the journey. Fortunately, my top hat was under my arm and saved these ladies sitting in front of us from disaster, since there was no time to open the window on the German girl's side. Of course, she was very distressed that because of her I had lost my hat, thrown out the window, but thanks to this small sacrifice, I obtained the favor of my fellow travellers and went the whole way with them on friendly terms. However, a rather unpleasant surprise awaited me in Taurog-

96

gen. When they asked us passengers to the office to receive our passports, the official disclosed to me that I would have to pay 30 rubles since on going abroad I had paid for only half a year and had spent three and one-half years abroad. I had not calculated upon this in Heidelberg and, with paying for my place in the coach, I had left in my pocket only a few rubles on which to subsist to Petersburg. The passenger from the front compartment was standing next to me—I had met him at the station but had not spoken a word to him before this moment, since I had been the ladies' servant—and he rescued me. This passenger turned out to be the cellist Davidov, who was going to Petersburg from the Leipzig Conservatory and had already delighted a Berlin audience on this trip. He helped me right there at the station to find a certain respectable elderly Jew who gave me 30 rubles for my gold watch as a pawn. We arrived in Petersburg at nine o'clock in the evening, February 1, 1860. At the post station, the husband of the French modiste, Mme. Allin, met her. I was introduced to him as a fellow traveller who had done her a number of services on the road, and I was invited by them to next Sunday's dinner in Mikhaylov Street, where I was entertained, as I remember now, by very good vol-au-vent and roast turkey. In return for this, I invited the husband and wife later for luncheon with Yeliseyev oysters and, with this, our acquaintanceship was ended. My older sister was married to officer Mikhaylovskiy of the Finnish regiment, of which I had long known, learning of it while still in the engineering college as a cadet, upon leaving, and then as a guard officer. They lived in the regiment's barracks, on the nineteenth line of Vasil'yev Island, and took me into their home from the second day of my arrival. I had to go on foot from here almost from the end of Vasil'yev Island, about three times to Glebov on the Vyborg side—at first to introduce myself to him, and then on the occasion of the printing of my dissertation, which was ready. While I was still abroad I received a letter from Glebov in which he promised to place me with the medical academy for defense of my thesis. Recalling the details at this time, I cannot help recalling the words said once by our famous chemist Nikolay Nikolayevich Zinin (a member of the Academy of Sciences and Professor of Chemistry at the Medical Academy, as well as its scientific secretary—the second person after the President) in answer to our (Botkin's and my) complaints on several aspects of Russian life: "Eh, youth, youth," he said as if seriously, but of course agreeing with us, "do you know that Russia is the only country where one can do anything."

I remember this saying because I did not present the dissertation to anyone, Glebov took my manuscript to his study and, without any request from me, it was printed free in the *Military-Medical Journal* and was defended by me no more than a month after I came to Petersburg. At the public debate I became acquainted with one of my critics, Evgeniy Ventseslavovich Pelikan, still a young man, a former professor of forensic medicine in the medical academy and just made director of the medical department of the ministry of internal affairs. He was a very intelligent man, a well-educated medical man for that time (at this very time he was giving lectures on some sections of physiology in the Passage), and we remained great friends until the end of his life. He introduced me to Professor Krasovskiy's family and acquainted me there with a young military doctor, whom I remember only from two stories from the times of Emperor Nikolay.

The first concerned himself, when he was still a very young intern of the first land hospital. Once while he was on duty, the sovereign unexpectedly came to the hospital. According to the regulations, the doctor on duty had to report that everything was all right, so many patients on hand, and so many for discharge. The point of well being, of course, went off all right, but he did not know about the other two and was compelled to answer both points of the Tsar's question with lack of knowledge. "Tell your chief that I said *fool* to you," said the sovereign, and he passed around the ward not saying a word. The head doctor was absent and, when he returned, the ill-fated intern had to repeat the sovereign's words. But the matter was not finished even with this. The next day, the head doctor took him to Yenokhin, the chief military-medical inspector, and he had to repeat the sovereign's words again.

The other incident happened with his friend, who served in a certain military hospital of the Western Region. During one of his trips west, the sovereign for some reason turned aside from his itinerary noted in advance, and came unexpectedly to this hospital just as the storyteller's friend was on duty. By the storyteller's words, this was a very clever and efficient fellow, but an eternal debauchee without money and, for that reason, he often did not go on duty in turn after his friends. This day, he was loafing in the duty room as usual, going on guard in an overcoat instead of a frock coat. When he was informed with fear that the sovereign was coming, he did not lose his head, but seized a bandage and a kit in the duty room, and ordered the one who had run up to inform the sovereign that the man on duty was with a patient; he had run to the first patient he came upon, thrown off his overcoat, and in only his shirt and pants had begun to prepare the hand for blood-letting. They brought the sovereign to this very bed, and the doctor, silently and not taking his eyes from his work, let the soldier's blood. The sovereign silently watched the whole operation to the end, then clapping him on the shoulder said, "Fine fellow," and went out, accompanied by the head doctor who had come at this time to look over the hospital. The sovereign left satisfied and ordered the doctor on duty to be presented a reward.

After the defense of my thesis, the business of my decision in the medical academy began. Zagorskiy, then professor of physiology, retired, and Yakubovich was appointed in his place; I could enter the same department as a junior scientific assistant. According to the academy's regulations at that time, the graduate student in the physiology department had to take an examination in this science and in zoology and comparative anatomy. When Zinin told me about this, I agreed to take the examination on physiology, but I refused the one in zoology, since I had not studied this subject. He reassured me, however, saying that it was a trifle, a pure formality. Only two examiners sat at this examination: Zagorskiy, the old academician Brandt who gave zoology in the medical academy, and Zinin. Zagorskiy had a talk with me for a couple of minutes, and Brandt asked me if I knew the principal work on infusoria. I answered that the name of Ehrenburg was of course familiar to me but I had not read his work since I had not studied zoology. I could not answer and could not take the second question, declaring that I had not studied zoology at all, and let the officials know about this, and I could not be examined. Zinin began to whisper with the elderly man, and the sitting ended. They soon took me as a junior scientific assistant in the physiology department and set me to giving lectures until the end of the academic year.

Reflecting now on whether I deserved a chair of experimental science at that time, I say according to my conscience, less than our assistants now who have not been abroad. They are acquainted with physiological practice in very diverse directions, but I for the present was only able to use frogs, and saw, it is true, many experiments in Ludwig's laboratory, sometimes even assisting in them, but I myself was really acquainted only with those methods which were linked with my work. They took me because there were not yet any such assistants in Russia and I, with all my limited knowledge, was nevertheless the first of the Russians who had partaken of Western science with such leading figures as my teachers in Germany. In this latter respect, even many Germans later envied me.

At first, the following circumstance helped me. Studying in Berlin, I had ordered a galvanometer from Sauerwald for electrophysiological studies, had obtained a stimulating apparatus from Du Bois-Reymond, his supports for experiments with frogs, and brought all these with me to Russia, knowing already how to use them. Therefore, fulfilling the order to begin the lecturing immediately on receipt of the position, I could begin giving lectures on organic electricity, not known to anyone in Russia at that time. The following circumstance may exemplify to what degree their study was a novelty for Russia at that time. I worked out the lectures in detail, word for word, and because of this I had the opportunity of printing them during the year in the *Military-Medical Journal*. I do not know who advised me, but this work was presented for some prize in the Academy of Sciences, and I received 700 rubles for it.

Toward spring, Bekkers came to the Academy and, after him, Botkin, and these men were taken as junior scientific assistants without entrance examinations—the first in the surgical clinic of the fourth year and Botkin in the therapeutic clinic of the same year.

It would be appropriate at this time to say a few words about our fate in coming to the Academy. A triumvirate stood at the head of the Academy: Dubovitskiy, Glebov, Zinin—all three middle aged people. President of the Academy Dubovitskiy was a very wealthy landowner, a zealous campaigner out of honor and, being near the war minister, Sukhozanet, he received large sums from the ministry for the organization of public services and amenities of the medical academy. He was not strong in learned matters, but he did not need to be—he had two helpers for this. He himself, as a great bustler, abandoned himself to tireless concerns over external order and administration of the vast institution entrusted to him. His troubles, it is true, were many. The Academy buildings had not been repaired since the time of their rise in the time of Emperor Paul; all the other structures, including the terrible anatomy theater, were of wood; all had fallen into decay and Dubovitskiy, a passionate lover of building day and night, troubled about putting up new buildings. He had already laid the foundation—a separate building was constructed for the physics and chemistry laboratory and the small fourth year clinics (the fifth year clinics were in the land hospital attached to the Academy) were renovated.

But the matter did not stop with this. In the first ten years of our stay in the Academy, he built the spacious Villier clinics and the anatomical-physiological institute. Before our entrance, the staff of professors in its turn demanded renovations. Elderly men lived the rest of their days in some departments, and there were no young forces. Dubovitskiy had been a professor in Kazan' at the same time as Zinin and honored him as a great scholar, evidently giving the work of renewing the staff of professors to him. One of the first people Zinin helped was his close friend, Glebov (they had studied together abroad when they were young), from Moscow—Glebov had a 25-year service record in the university—and they began to be active in the direction indicated. From his pupils at the Academy, Zinin began to prepare the future chemist, Borodin, and the future physicist, Khlebnikov, and he evidently gave the medical renovation over to Glebov. Glebov, as a Moscow professor, could have known only Muscovites. He probably knew us or heard about us from friends as Botkin, Bekkers and I were the first Russian pupils abroad. After the end of Emperor Nikolay's reign, the sending of medical men abroad at government expense stopped. All this together was the reason for our being taken into the Academy.

I went to Moscow at Shrovetide to meet old friends, and I saw also my former servant, my friend Fifochka, now Feofan Vasil'yevich Devyatnin.

Over a small decanter of vodka and hors d'oeuvres in the Great Moscow Hotel, where I stayed, he told me the story of his successes from the time when we had parted, and about how the fame of his skill as a shoemaker, spread by the clergy from parish to parish, finally reached Boris and Gleb, where as a priest's pupil he had found a bride with a dowry which placed him on his feet. Now he had a workers' association and he was one of Korolev's suppliers. His wife turned out to be a very efficient woman and not only knew how to handle the association but even learned cutting out, i.e., to be chief of the shoemaking business, and she knew how to keep her husband at attention if he happened to start drinking. When, at the end of the lunch, I began to treat him to cigarettes, he treated me to a real Havana cigar, which he had brought with him on purpose, declaring that he could not help having a small stock of such cigars on him because after each dealing of goods to a firm, the entertainment of the head salesman invariably followed, with lunch at an inn and a Havana cigar at the end. On saying goodbye, I heard from him the following words: "Well, Ivan Mikhaylovich, I was Fifochka to you before, now I have become Feofan Vasil'yevich. You have become better, as it were, in appearance but worse in your soul—you do not have your former simplicity." He was right, of course, recalling former times when I shared joys and grief with him, and comparing the past with the impression of the present moment.

I was given a laboratory on the lower floor of the outer wing, next to the anatomy theater. It consisted of two large rooms which had formerly served as a chemical laboratory. Therefore, in the first room off the entrance there was a hood, and in the other, along the wall with two windows, stood a table which took up the whole length of the wall, and over the table were shelves (evidently for reagents) in the pier between the windows. Whether there were any instruments besides knives, scissors and pincers in the room I do not remember, but probably there were few. This was no great misfortune, however—the Academy budget was generous, 200,000 rubles and Dubovitskiy was not stingy in issuing instruments. Much later I learned of still one more property of my laboratory: under the room where I spent 8 years was a deserted cellar with stagnant water which froze in winter and slowly thawed out during the rest of the year. To this cellar I owed an illness which lasted for an entire half of the '60's and of which I was cured only in Odessa.

I was in Simbirsk province during the summer with my family and became acquainted with the new members of my family—the husband of one of my sisters, Doctor Kasten, a physician on Pashkov's neighboring estate, the wife of one of my brother's and their small daughter, Natasha. I was greeted fondly by all and lived with them in a corresponding way. This was, I believe, a most happy time for the members of the family living in the country. All were still young, lived without want, and as good people, were loved by those around them. I carry such an impression from this trip.

My real professorship in the Medical Academy began during the fall of 1860. I have several leaflets from that time which bear witness to the fact that I wrote my lectures out word for word. I have found from the leaflets that I gave: circulation of the blood, respiration, absorption of substances from the alimentary canal, classification, the plastic movements of the body and muscle physiology. The blood, digestion and the nervous system were taken by the regular professor of physiology, Yakubovich, essentially a histologist.[1] It has been interesting to glance over these long-forgotten leaflets after 43 years. It turns out that I was not able to distinguish the important from the secondary in all cases, I could not designate exactly in words the various concepts, and I was distinguished in general by my inclination towards anecdotal, sometimes even very narrow opinions. There were some naïvetes, but the German textbooks saved me from gross mistakes.

In addition to writing and reading of lectures, I prepared my essays on organic electricity for print that year.

The year 1861 was memorable, I believe, to everyone who lived in Petersburg at that time. Everyone knew that the great act of freeing millions of serfs was put through and all anxiously awaited its promulgation. For some time things breathed much easier than before, in literature and in society there arose new needs, new demands for life. But during this year the general mood, as before the great occasion, was tense, quiet, biding its time, without any outbursts. This wave, of course, concerned us, too, but we were newcomers to the city without connections in literary circles, and we celebrated this year in a family manner, so to speak, in our own small circle, rejoicing at the free trends of this era and taking a great interest in the alluring prospects of the walks of life just opened before us. This was, of course, a very happy time.

In the summer of 1861 I stayed in Petersburg, lived on Vyborg Street, walked to my laboratory and studied problems on the way, of whether edible mushrooms did not contain poisonous substances. Upon order I was brought a sieve of russula, and I treated them in the following manner: I cooked them cut in very small pieces in water, strained off the slimy broth, fried it with a lead acetate and hydrogen sulfide, and steamed the solution almost dry. From a great quantity of mushrooms came a small quantity of dark brown liquid of a weakly acid reaction. One drop of it in a spinal lymph node of a frog was enough to evoke a stoppage of the heart. In other words, I dealt with muscarine, later-discovered in death-caps, but I was not able to obtain

[1] He had studied in Dorpat, was studying the microscopic structure of the spinal cord, was introduced by his teacher, Reikhardt Humboldt, as a promising investigator of the structure of the central nervous system, received through Humboldt a mission abroad, and was appointed professor in place of Zagorskiy, who was retiring.

this substance from my solutions. I suggested to Borodin that he study this, but for some reason he refused.

In the winter of 1861 misfortune befell two of the members of our circle. Botkin became ill with serious typhus but, thank heavens, began to get better after six weeks. Poor Bekkers, suffering almost the whole winter with heart disease which did not appear pathological as such, finished the end of the winter tragically. This year I lived in the same apartment with him and we lived so that we met only at dinner and sometimes in the evening when we went to the same place as guests. After a year's stay in Petersburg, he had a small practice and several acquaintances.

A very handsome and well brought up young man with good manners (he was from a French-German family), a gallant admirer of ladies who spoke French like a Frenchman, in all an extraordinarily kind and mild man, his friends and patients could not but like him. This accounts for the fact that he rarely sat at home in the evenings and often returned very late, when I had already gone to bed. It was necessary to get up early and, upon arriving home, to prepare lectures. I knew that he mercilessly ordered the servant to wake him, pulling the blanket off him, but I found out only later that sometimes our servant found him sleeping in the morning in the armchair at the writing table. Such a life could not continue for long, more so since the heart illness was not mild, judging by his tired, tormented appearance in the middle of winter. About two months before his death, they brought me news (at this time Bekkers was at home): "For heaven's sake, follow Bekkers; he will kill himself." This time the matter was settled satisfactorily—he who brought the news himself prevented a catastrophe. Soon after this a relative came to him —a widow. He put her in his bedroom and he himself moved into the study. She spent about two weeks in his room, not leaving the room, recovering from the shock of her husband's death; then she left, but whether she left Moscow I do not know.

Bekkers was as if quieted and I had already stopped thinking about the past when suddenly in the morning of the ill-fated day at the end of 1861, when I was hardly dressed, I heard a call of unusual tone. I ran in, Bekkers pointed to his writing table with the words "potassium cyanide" and "my will," tore his tie from his neck, went into the bedroom and threw himself onto the bed. To my words, "let me put my finger in your mouth to make you vomit," he succeeded only in saying that he did not want to live, and after about five minutes was no more. Who and what killed this golden heart I do not know, but it was probably not any professional failure in the Academy.

While I was still abroad I heard about the striving for higher education which had arisen among Russian women and I returned to Russia with ready sympathy for such a movement. In the fall of 1861 I became acquainted with two women spokesmen of the new trend who were seriously and firmly set on the deed of service to the women's question. They demonstrated this later, finishing the course in Zurich and passing the examination in Russia for the right to practice. At that time, they had already prepared for the examination for a boys' gymnasium course, on which they spent their evenings, and in the mornings they went to the Medical Academy, at that time accessible to women, where they heard several professors (including myself, incidentally) and worked in the anatomical theater of the stern Gruber, who was, however, pleased with their studies. How could one not help these worthy toilers!

For the sake of maintaining their energies at the end of the academic year, I gave both of them such topics which demanded very little preparatory information and could be worked out by them in their homes. One's problem was that the wearing of glasses with colored glass evokes color blindness for the rays of a given refraction and to compare the results obtained with the known symptoms of congenital color blindness. The other was to study the influence of tetanization of the skin on light tactile stimulations in the interpolar space and outside it. Both of these works were printed in the same year in Russian and the year following in German.

The third event of this year was N. N. Zinin's attempt to introduce me into the Academy of Sciences, which began without any knowledge on my part. I will tell about it in the way in which I found out about it, although not fully, later. Baer occupied the chair of anatomy and physiology in the Academy, and probably he wanted to prepare a successor to himself, because rumors reached me later that he intended for Kühne to be the candidate for his place. Probably the Russian party objected to this and, for their part, advanced me as a possible candidate. Evidently, Baer had to yield, but he yielded conditionally, deferring the question to a more detailed friendship with me. Probably with this aim, the old academician Brandt, who lectured in zoology in the Medical Academy, was instructed to invite me to be at his place as a friend at the Medical Academy. I cannot otherwise explain where such a wish of his could have appeared—not from the examination itself, which I so brilliantly passed with him upon entering the Medical Academy. Not suspecting anything, I came to his family on the designated days several times and always found there two German academicians—Schiffner and Kunick.

There were discussions, of course, in German, but without any perceptible approaches to learn my line of thinking or the degree of my learning. This was probably a test for the degree of my culture because inquiries were made by the German professors about my learning—Pflüger told me this directly much later. Be that as it may, Zinin told me once, probably upon receiving such inquiries, that I as a physiologist ought to introduce myself to such a famous and respectable representative of the same science in Russia as Baer, and he took me to him hat in hand. After this, he himself told me that they wanted to select me for the Academy. Knowing the real value of this, I understood that they were choosing me according to the proverb: "Among the blind, the one-eyed is king." Moreover, I did not have any basis for thinking that I would turn out worthy of such a high honor even in my subsequent activity. I did not want to live with red ears and for this reason flatly refused. Soon after this, Middendorf, the permanent secretary of the Academy, came to me at my apartment with Bekkers to talk me into changing my decision, but wishing to end it at once, I said to him that I did not intend to devote myself exclusively to a learned career and would be engaged in medical practice. With this the matter was ended. It seems that during this same winter, I built a manometer for determining the average value of blood pressure and performed experiments with it.

However fate treated me during this year, my memory of the freedom of life abroad still did not die out, and it pulled me to such an extent into the open that in the summer, when I had finished all my studies, I received a year's leave (with the consent of Professor Yakubovich to take upon himself for a certain fee my share of the lectures), and in the fall of 1862 I was already in Paris to study and work under Claude Bernard. I arrived there before the laboratories were open and used my free time to go via Marseilles, along the delightful Mediterranean Sea to heavenly Naples. Intending to spend only a very short time there, I put myself into the hands of a guide as soon as I arrived and visited all the sights of the city and its environs including, of course, the summit of Vesuvius, Pompei, the Blue Grotto on Capri, and the Dog Grottos on the Bayshore. Later I became much better acquainted with Naples, but this time I was there nine days in all. On the return trip to Marseilles on a small steamship of the Italian company Rubatino, a fierce but not dangerous mistral rather rocked us, and we were a very long time in transit. The ship came into Marseilles at night. There was not a single carriage on the wharf, and I was forced to take as a guide a boy whom I summoned to take me to a nearby hotel where, in his words, the Spanish bishops always stopped. The room I received had probably not seen Spanish visitors for a long time, however, because I had hardly laid down on the bed and put out the candle when hundreds of hungry bedbugs began to tear me to pieces. I speak without any exaggeration because when I lit the candle I saw the whole herd with my own eyes. I rang for the porter to get another room.

Bernard's laboratory (at the Collège de France) consisted of a small room in which he himself worked and an auditorium adjacent to it. In the workroom in the first place stood a vivisection table and several cupboards with vessels and instruments, and in the auditorium in front of the benches for the audience was the professor's table on a small platform. I received permission to work at this table. During the whole winter of my stay there, beside Bernard and his assistant Leconte, there were only the old retired military doctor, M. Rancheval, a warm admirer of Bernard, and myself. This lonely old man without a family was probably bored at home and came to the laboratory almost every day. Bernard regarded him with a tender smile, sometimes gave him pincers for him to help with during operations and apparently gave the old man great pleasure by this. When he had become acquainted with me, M. Rancheval took a seat near me during my experiments. He was a republican, an ardent hater of Napoleon III, and he and I had not a little fling concerning this "scoundrel and rascal of December 2."

The day was spent in the laboratory in the following manner. In the morning at about nine o'clock I arrived. The hall porter of the college opened the entrance to the laboratory for me, and I set to work with the frogs either alone or in the company of the republican until Bernard came to his workroom, which occurred about 1:00 p.m. His assistant came with him, preparations were made for experiments at the vivisection table and were performed. I was admitted to them as an observer and withdrew to the auditorium when they were done. At this time, Bernard's friend, Bertelo, who was already famous at that time but not yet a member of the Academy, although he was already a professor in the Collège de France, very often came to Bernard. I was not present at their discussions and was never even presented to Bertelo. Bernard treated me politely, of course, but he regarded my work completely indifferently. The only instances of our discussions were questions on his part of how they look in Germany on one or another subject of interest to him. I must note that he did not know German and was only very little acquainted with German literature on physiology. At his lectures I heard only two German names, Valentin and Virchow. A year after I came, Kühne came to him and became intimate with him. Through Kühne, Bernard became acquainted with the Germans[2]—I heard this from Kühne himself. Bernard was a superior worker in physiology and was considered the most skillful vivisectionist in Europe (as I believe our famous physiologist Ivan Petrovich Pavlov is considered now); with all this a very keen observer (as it is said, for example, in his experiments with innervation of the salivary gland), and a sober philospher. But he was not such a teacher as the Germans, and he worked out the topics which arose in his mind with his own hands, not leaving his study,

[2] Everything described concerns the time before the German pogrom, when the French in general inadequately estimated what was done beyond France's boundaries, but in the period following this, the insufficient knowledge of German by the French continued to tell. I know for certain that at the time when Koch's discovery of tuberculins as an antituberculosis measure excited all Europe, the colleagues of our famous Mechnikov asked him to translate the magazine articles which poured out in Germany at that time.

so to speak. This is why it was impossible for someone such as myself who came to him for a short time to learn anything in his laboratory.

This winter Regnier gave a course on thermometry in the Collège de France, and I sat at his lectures. During this course, which was instructive in the highest degree, he described, in part, one modification of his air thermometer, making it possible for the observer to measure the temperature of the soil or layers of air over it at any time sitting in his study. In this modification, the manometer remained in the observer's room and an air cylinder went outside by means of a very thin metal tube of any length, if only several meters. I, as a man who had spent much time with Lothar Meyer's crude absorptiometer (where the receiver for the absorbing liquid also connected with the manometer, but by means of a rubber tube) and who in fact knew its deficiencies, immediately had the thought of using the thin metal tube for the structure of the absorptiometer, which I later did. For such a purpose, I brought a very large supply of such tubes from Paris.

My thoughts about gases were diverted for many years, moreover, by the experiments which I did in Bernard's laboratory, in company with dear M. Rancheval. Their description requires a small preface.

The question of how the will is capable not only of evoking but also of repressing movements has been noted probably from the time when people began to notice in themselves and their neighbors the ability to depress "involuntarily" impulses to movements (for example, a cough or sneeze, movements from itching or pain, etc.) and to withstand in general any temptation for various actions. The role of the nervous system in movements had long ago become a subject of scientific investigation, but the first ray in the dark field of depression of movements was cast only in 1845 with Ed. Weber's memorable work with the inhibiting action of the vagus nerve on the heart. In this work he established two facts: the acceleration of the heartbeat after cutting the nerve, and its slowing down to a full diastolic stop upon excitation of the distal segment of the cut nerve, from which he concluded that normally weak excitations from the cerebrum must travel continuously along the nerve moderating the activity of the heart. Along with this he noticed in passing that the intensification (already known at that time) of spinal reflexes following the separation of the spinal cord from the cerebrum happens probably in the same way, that is, that normally weak inhibitory influences on the reflex activity of the spinal cord derive from the cerebrum. As a proof of what great interest was aroused by Weber's discovery in Germany, there was a hubbub 10 years later accompanying a second similar discovery by Pflüger with the action of the great cranial nerve on the movements of the intestine. Weber's note concerning the cerebrum and spinal cord remained as if unnoticed but meanwhile a series of exploratory experiments were soon begun upon this problem. There were two reasons for this: on the one hand, from the experiments of Helmholtz and Du Bois-Reymond, the attention of the German physiologists was long diverted from the nerve centers in favor of the more easily accessible investigation of nerves; on the other hand, the Germans made too much of experiments on the cerebrum from the time when experiments in this region by Magendie, Longet, and Schiff were giving confused and contradictory results (for example, various ablations of the central portions of the brain with ensuing disturbances of locomotion).

There were comments from Ludwig in Germany on the occasion of these experiments: "It is equivalent to studying the mechanism of a watch, shooting at it with a gun." Be that as it may, no one confirmed Weber's earlier observation until 1861, when experimental verification of his proposition came to be my lot. Thanks to Türck's very simple and reliable method, which already existed at the time, of measuring on a frog the ease of elicitation of cutaneous-muscular reflexes, I used this animal for my experiments.

The form of the experiments, in terms of the nature of the work, was very simple: section the cerebrum from the front, measure the reflexes after each section, apply stimulation to the exposed cross section of the cerebrum and measure the reflexes again. At first I tried to apply electrical stimulation to the cerebrum,[3] but this method turned out to be very unsatisfactory and even of little use and, therefore, was replaced by chemical stimulation of the cross sections with sodium chloride, the action of which is restricted for a long time to the surface stimulated, not penetrating into the depth of the brain (which cannot be said about stimulation by electric current, however weak it might be). Attention, of course, was paid to the fact that the effects obtained were associated with stimulation of definite places and did not depend on pain propagated to the cerebrum, the conclusion being that in the frog brain centers exist from which inhibiting influences on the reflex activity of the spine originate.

I called these centers "Centres modérateurs de l'action réflexe" in French and "Hemmungscentra" in German, and later this caused attacks on the interpretation of these experiments. In France this work remained little noticed at the time of its publication, but in Germany, where I went from Paris, my work met with a warm welcome. First I showed the experiments in detail to Ludwig, in the presence of Preyer (then professor of physiology in Jena), working at that time with Ludwig. Both, but especially Preyer, were pleased with my explanations. I then showed the work to Brücke at his request and, finally, on a trip to Berlin, to Du Bois-Reymond, who met me and was very friendly.

[3] I cannot but recall here with gratitude the delightful, good old man, Rumkaupf, who, at my request to rent a small induction apparatus, gave me his for an indefinite period of time for nothing, taking no deposit, of course.

The demonstration and explanation in connection with my work went so satisfactorily even here that it was concluded with questions from the professor on an extraneous subject, namely, about the liberation of Russian women —the works of my lady pupils were printed in German journals and were already known to Du Bois-Reymond. He did not understand the reasons for such a liberation movement since he had never had occasion to hear that women were dissatisfied with their position and were striving to stand on their own feet. This was even less understood by my young German friends of former times. They even laughed at it, not having a presentiment that in due course university doors would be open to women in Germany, earlier than in Russia.

I returned to Petersburg in May 1863 and spent all summer writing *Reflexes of the Brain*, which was to play a considerable role in my life.

In my doctoral dissertation in 1860, are the following two statements: "All movements bearing the name of voluntary in physiology are reflex in a strict sense;" and, "the most common characteristic of normal activity of the brain (as far as it is expressed in movement) is the discrepancy between the stimulation and the action and movement evoked by it."

The first statement is clear by itself, but the second requires the following brief explanation. Beyond the influence of the brain, the stimulations sensed and the reflex movements they evoke go parallel to one another, according to strength, i.e., the weak movements correspond to the weak stimulations and vice versa. Under the influence of the brain, however, there is no such correlation—a weak stimulation can evoke a very strong movement (such as the flinching of the whole body at an unexpected light touch) and, on the contrary, a very strong stimulation can be expressed by no movement (when, for example, a person endures great pain without flinching). If one adds to this the fact that a candidate for a doctor's degree could not but know the tri-member composition of reflexes and the psychological significance of the middle member in acts concluding with a voluntary movement, it then follows that my thought about the transference of psychic phenomena, from the nature of their mechanism, to a physiological basis must have strayed through my mind during my first stay abroad, the more so since as a student I had studied psychology.

There is no doubt that these thoughts flowed through my mind even during my stay in Paris because I set to work on experiments which had a direct relation to acts of consciousness and will. Be that as it may, on my return to Petersburg from Paris these thoughts evidently settled in my mind, partly definite, partly as hypothetical propositions, in the following sequence: in daily conscious and unconscious life, man cannot dismiss influences of feeling on himself from without via his sense organs and of sensations coming from his own body (feeling oneself). All his mental life, with all its manifestations of movement, is supported by them because, with the loss of all sensations, mental life is impossible (the last proposition was confirmed about twenty years later by very rare instances of observations of people with loss of almost all their feelings). Just as action of sense organs is a determinant of movement, in psychic life, wishes and desires are the determinants of actions; both reflexes and mental acts, passing into action, bear the characteristic of expediency; some influence felt from without always serves as the basis of reflexes: the same sort of thing, though often imperceptible to us, takes place in relation to emotional movements generally, (for without sensory influences, psychic influences are impossible!); in the majority of cases, reflexes are concluded with movements; but there are those for which inhibition of movement serves as an end; the same thing follows in mental acts: the majority are expressed in imagery or by an act; but there are a great number of cases where the goals of these are inhibited and a tri-member act takes on the appearance of a bi-member one—the meditative intellectual side of life has this form; passions are rooted, directly or indirectly, in the so-called sensory systems of man, capable of increasing to the degree of strong desires (hunger, self-preservation, sexual feeling, etc.), and are manifested by very abrupt actions or deeds; therefore, they can be treated in the category of reflexes with an intensified result.

These propositions laid the groundwork which served as the basis for the small treatise I wrote, *An Attempt to Bring Physiological Bases into Mental Processes*. The editor of the medical newspaper to which I gave my manuscript for publication told me that the censor demanded a change in the title, and in place of the former title, I inserted *Reflexes of the Brain*. [Because of this book, I was made out to be an unintentional champion of undisciplined temper and a nihilist philosopher. Unfortunately, a frank explanation of these misunderstandings in print was impossible at the time because of the censorship rules which existed, but it was not difficult to remove them. Indeed, in its most narrow form, such an accusation could have taken this view: each act, regardless of its content, is considered by this theory prepared beforehand by the nature of the given person; completion of the act is ascribed to a certain, perhaps completely insignificant stimulus from without, and the act itself is considered unavoidable, from which it follows that even a criminal is not at fault for the evil deeds he has done; this is not enough, however; the doctrine loosens the hands of the wanton man for whatever disreputable business he wishes, convincing him beforehand that he will not be guilty for he cannot help doing what he has conceived.

The point of loosening hands for any disreputable act is the fruit of the direct misunderstandings. In the incriminated work, the reflexes which are concluded with inhibition of movements are placed on an equal footing side by side with reflexes which are concluded by movements. If the completion of good acts on moral grounds corresponds to the first, then corresponding to the second is a person's resistance to any impulses in general, and consequently, to bad impulses. In my treatise there was no need to speak about good and evil; I was talking about actions in general, and it was maintained only that under certain given conditions both action and inhibition of action inevitably take place by the law of necessary connection between cause and effect. Just where is the implication of lack of discipline here? I had to speak regarding the accusation that the concept of guilt and punishability was eliminated by my study at a dinner in Odessa during the 70's, given by Dr. Münch in honor of the arrival of his friend, a celebrated Moscow lawyer whose name I do not remember. The lawyer told me directly that my study had destroyed the element of guilt and had eliminated the element of punishability. To this I answered: maintaining the irresponsibility of the person for the guilt of this action in general, I consider equally not guilty the criminal in his actions and the power to punish him; but crime as an evil I do not excuse, and the various steps of depravity of criminals and their unfitness for a life of freedom I do not deny. Consequently, I recognize the right of authority to protect society from evil.]

Although I was made out to be a nihilist philosopher because of this little book, and the book itself was acknowledged as unfit for general use, if not absolutely deleterious, I nevertheless will not go into any explanation of this, since a frank discussion in print of the several points in the book which were incriminated would be impossible in light of the rules of the censor even in the future, when these recollections will be published after my death. I will limit myself only to the following: during the forty years since its appearance in print, I have not heard of a single instance, thank heavens, in which it has moved anyone to evil because of a false understanding of its points.[4]

Upon my return to Petersburg in 1863 I began to lead a settled life (I of course became wealthier). I found a clean, three-room apartment, started a simple home of my own, ate at home and even began to call in friends for the evening from time to time, and we jokingly called these "balls," since nothing could be counted on except for the illumination of the rooms until day and tea and sweets from Babikov,[5] who was at that time inescapable for all the

---

[4] If the text enclosed in brackets is passed by the censor, this paragraph is not necessary; otherwise it is to be used (I. M. Sechenov's note under the title, "No. 13.").

[5] During this modest entertainment, lapses occurred which, with the youth of the company, served as fun and not as chagrin. The chief salesman, Babikov, was a merchant of the old stock and at every opportunity strived to palm off something good for nothing as good. To the reproaches of the customer, he usually answered calmly: "It is our business to sell, and it is your business to look." This was well-known to my guests, of course.

inhabitants of the foundry district. During this time, certain Saturdays, well known from the description of his friend, N. A. Belogolovyy, were arranged at Botkin's. Both of us started up new friendships, and life began to flow for long years as it does for all working people in general—the week for work, and then rest among a group of friends. Our friends at that time were all good people, workers like ourselves, not in need of any special embellishments for the weekend rest except simple, friendly discussion. In all the next seven years I remember only two parties with dancing—one arranged by engagement in the Hotel Kley hall, and the other at Botkin's home.

Of my new friends I knew the Grubers, husband and wife, particularly well, and first I will describe this original couple. While he was a professor in the medical academy, Pirogov sent for Girtle's assistant from Prague, Gruber, and appointed him anatomical dissector in the Medical Academy. Without knowledge of the language and customs and regulations of the academy environment (rather vague at that time), and being highly impractical in ordinary life, Gruber was bound to make blunders frequently, not acting or speaking in the manner of his associates. From the first years of his stay in Russia, he was under the impression that he was surrounded by enemies. If my just demands were fulfilled from time to time, he said, there was always the addition: "Oh, this accursed German!" This addition was, of course, joking in many cases, but he took it seriously. His wholehearted love for anatomy, and the wealth of anatomical material that fell into his hands, which he could not have dreamed of abroad, held Gruber in Russia. He knew only anatomy, considered it one of the foundations upon which the universe stood, and from morning until night studied only those things (anomalies of the structure of the body) which demanded enormous material, since he wished not only to find the comparatively rare anomalies but to keep statistics upon them, i.e., to determine the numerical relation of the anomalies to the normal. In this respect, the daily studies of hundreds of students in the anatomical theater were a treasure to him. During the first years he bought a record book in which he kept data on all outstanding preparations and the number of anomalies noted in them by himself, by his assistants, and even by the doctor's assistant, who was trained for these searches. In the course of time this book naturally reached colossal dimensions and was a treasure, the custody of which was entrusted only to the principal and most favored of his assistants. If this person fell into disfavor, the treasure was taken away from him.[6] The

---

[6] A similar but more original instance of love for a notebook comes from Ludwig. This happened in Heidelberg during the '20's of the last century. The well-known chemist and Privy Councillor Tideman had a notebook in which he entered all the impressions and thoughts which came to his mind. He had a young daughter of marriageable age, and a young assistant, Bischoff, who was later well known. The daughter and the assistant fell in love with each other and for a long time feared the severity of the Privy Councillor,

feeling of duty which resulted from the knowledge that he was the source of anatomical knowledge, and the feeling of justice, was developed in Gruber to a degree incomprehensible to us Russians. Thus, in his daily examinations of many persons in giving out preparations for the student doctors and the military doctors attached to the academy, he dismissed people after the fifth failure, not admitting them to a sixth trial. In this way, all his life was spent in continuous examinations and in the description of irregularities. One particularly fortunate year he told us with pride, knocking his fist on the table, that he had written Hundert-vierzig Abhandlungen (140 articles)! From the beginning, Virchow had published his articles in his journal, but when they poured down like rain he refused and Gruber himself had them published as separate reprints. Considering himself a man worthy of esteem, he loved celebrations in his honor and prepared fiery speeches for them and himself described them in German (these descriptions, it seems, were published by Braumüller in Vienna). Good at heart, he conducted himself very strictly in the anatomical theater, commanding his subordinates abruptly. He even demanded that they meet him at the station when he returned to Petersburg from abroad after vacation. He had adopted these traits from his teacher, Girtle, before whom he himself had trembled in former times, and he generally considered himself an unlimited sovereign in the anatomical theater (the students called him the Vyborg Emperor).

It cost me much effort once to try to convince him that he did not have the right to dismiss an assistant appointed to him by the authorities. Eternally busy with his anatomy and his anomalies, he looked at all the rest as if casually, and catching in the people around him only the most conspicuous features, he divided these people into the following categories: alte Esel[7]—these were all the former old professors of the academy, with the inclusion of one present academician; Schweinsköpfe[8]—all those ill-disposed in the anatomical theater; Lausbuben[9]—unpleasant young people; gute Kerle[10]—first-class friends; and pfiffige Kerle[11]—Gruber's favorites, among whom he ranked Pirogov and Botkin. Pirogov earned this title by his mockeries of the archaic procedures of the old-time academy, which were hateful to Gruber, and Botkin, by his gay cock-and-bull stories with which he liked to entertain Gruber, knowing his tastes.

---

but finally Bischoff decided to ask for the daughter's hand. Of course, he was driven away like Lausbul, for having thought of the Privy Councillor's daughter. The lovers thought and conjectured on this misfortune, and finally found a way to overcome it. The Privy Councillor lost his notebook; he ran about for several days like a madman, but becoming enlightened to the truth at last, said to his assistant, no longer wrathfully: "Well, take my daughter and give me my notebook," which was of course done.

[7] Old asses.   [8] Pigheads.   [9] Urchins.   [10] Good children.
[11] Clever children.

As a wife for this eccentric, God sent a woman who was also slightly eccentric in appearance but, in essence, of the highest qualities of the soul. To her "Mutzerle" (as she called her husband) she was utterly devoted as he was to anatomy; she was his nurse, on the alert so that nothing would disturb his work, helping him with it as much as she was able,[12] and often spending whole evenings in the anatomical theater with a stocking in her hands so as not to leave her child alone. Pure in soul, sincere, ardent and brave—later she proved this in deed, more than once saving students from danger—she always called a spade a spade, rebuked without putting up with any falsehood, but was ready to kiss young and old for any good deed. I am sure that in case of need she would have stood up in defense of her "Mutzerle" in the face of mortal danger. Although he loved her, he apparently did not notice that the poor woman's whole life was devoted to him, and drove her, with his unconscious egoism, to the point where she finally did not believe she could go alone, without her husband, to the theater or to visit friends. Personally, her more than 40 years of life in Russia did not bring her any joys, but her upright soul could not but love youth for its frequently rash, but always honest impulses towards good. As Gruber's wife, she grew fond of the academy for the respect shown her husband, and when she died, she willed almost all her wealth to the Medical Academy for student stipends. A great friend of Gruber and myself, Yevgeniy Ventseslavovich Pelikan, who by that time had already worked up to the rank of councillor of State and director of the medical department, and consequently had seen a great deal in his time, intending to go to Gruber's for a visit, said to me: "Let's go to the infants." Having been brought up on sweet food and beginning to put on weight, he was carried away with the Viennese schnitzels made by Madame Gruber, who had learned the art of cooking as a girl in Prague from a cook of a certain Czech magnate, and she loved to entertain Pelikan as a real connoisseur of her skill.

The men usually gathered at Botkin's on Saturdays, and Gruber was a Saturday habitué. I played the role of interpreter for the Gruber family for that which they did not understand in Russian life and, therefore, when we were at Botkin's, Gruber sat beside me so that he could come running for my help in case something in the conversation was not clear. When he got into such a bind, I received a punch in the side with the word "sic," and I knew what to do.

Before Pelikan became acquainted with our group, I knew him only superficially and by rumor. He belonged to the class of unfortunates who pass their youths in clover with a strong hand behind the back, and being gentle by

[12] One spring, for instance, Gruber needed a hare. Husti (as he called his wife) ran to almost all the markets and finally came across a vendor in Hay Market who was sharp, as merchants go, and sold her a rotten hare for 6 rubles. She herself told this story, amiably scolding her "Mutzerle" for his learned whims.

nature, give this hand the liberty to lead them along the path of worldly well being. Thus, at the end of medical school he was introduced into an aristocratic circle, appointed regimental doctor in a horse guard regiment, which also served as the nursery garden of the government people. Pelikan, by the way, took with him from here the belief that future government men drew their wisdom from the novels of Dumas-père.

Introduced in sufficient measure to this circle, he abandoned it, went abroad for improvement in the sciences and became a professor of forensic medicine with a view toward changing his learned career into a bureaucratic one at first opportunity. I do not know to what extent his personal tastes, and those imposed upon him from without, were important in this last transformation, but to our group, when he was already a prominent official, he did not have in him the personality of a bureaucrat. Having met us like old friends returning from abroad with interesting new things, he immediately became good friends with us and stood on an equal footing with us. I have already said elsewhere that on the way to Petersburg I found him, a department director, at lectures in a very modest auditorium in the Passage. During the first years of our life in Petersburg he founded the magazine Herald of Forensic Medicine with Lovtsov as editor. This was direct evidence of his love for his scientific affairs. Having in youth a supporting hand in back is, of course, handy and, perhaps, even useful if it pushes the young person on the real road, but I do not believe this happened in his case. On his own way he had to meet many temptations. Not being a fighter, he was probably forced from time to time to make concessions and turned into the type of man suppressed by his life practice who, however, preserved the ability to distinguish true good from official. I knew his real form of thought; the chivalrously honest Dr. Lovtsov, a member of Botkin's circle,[13] who had a lot of business with Pelikan concerning the editing of the magazine, was devoted to him with all his soul and always spoke highly of him as an excellent man. Finally, Madam Gruber, keen about all good, liked him, even though she knew of some transgressions in his past concerning women. By chance, Pelikan played a certain role even in my fate. Soon after I left the Medical Academy (I will speak about this later), Odessa University chose me as professor of physiology in the physico-mathematical department, but Ivan Davydovich Delyanov, who was substituting at that time for Count Tolstoy, who was on leave, did not make up his mind or did not want to settle the matter for almost half a year, from the fall of 1870 through the spring of 1871. In the spring of 1871, an international commission on the anticholeric problem was to meet in Constantinople, and Pelikan went there as the Russian government's delegate. On his trip via Odessa, he met the local

---

[13] Where he was called "the last of the marquis"—because of his subtlety of manner and chivalrous concepts of honor.

district trustee Golubtsov, and they had a conversation about me. Regarding this, I must note that Golubtsov was a medical man and Pelikan, as a prominent person in the medical world, had great importance in his eyes. Knowing by rumor that he was personally acquainted with me, Golubtsov was interested in finding out whether I really was a man dangerous and harmful for young people, and he added that this circumstance was hindering my appointment in the University. Pelikan even laughed at this and so convinced Golubtsov of my harmlessness that he took my appointment on his own responsibility, and I was approved. I heard this whole story from Pelikan himself.

I would like to speak well of one more close friend of that time, clever, vivacious, gifted Vladimir Kovalevskiy, who unfortunately ended his life too early because he lived too quickly. It is not in my power to paint his portrait, however—he was really too mobile and versatile, therefore I am limiting myself to an enumeration of his accomplishments, with a small illustration for each of them. Here are his qualifications in chronological order: a graduate from law school; a lover of natural science on leaving school; a translator; a prominent publisher of chiefly scientific-historical works (for example, Brehm's *Lives of Animals*); the disinterested liberator of Sofiya Vasil'yevna Krukovskaya from an imaginary parental yoke, which, however, gave her the opportunity to become a famous mathematician; a student of German for several years, returning from abroad a geologist; unsuccessfully, for his pocketbook, a builder of homes and a professor of geology who did not have time to rest in this quiet refuge. And these are illustrations of his characteristics. Lively as quicksilver with a head full of broad schemes, he could not live without starting out on some new enterprise and did this not with mercenary motives but in accordance with the restlessness of his nature irrepressibly pushing him to the side of prevailing trends in society. During these times the natural sciences were in vogue, and the demand for books of this type was very lively. As a lover of natural science, Kovalevskiy became a translator and little by little became involved in publishing activities. He began with pennies in his pocket and was carried away with his first successes, but his plans grew much faster than his profit, and Kovalevskiy went into full swing. He fought desperately, obtaining means, worked day and night and lived nearly in half starvation, but he did not lose heart. He gave up his publishing activity, not because it was impossible to continue but because he was going abroad with his wife to study. He gave his business to another publishing firm in a very neglected condition because he had conducted it in grand style by himself without assistants and had neglected the bookkeeping side of the enterprise. When affairs were disentangled, it turned out that he had published more than 100,000 rubles worth of books and could have had a large income if he had kept his accounts correctly.

Who does not know from the biographical data of Sofiya Vasil'yevna what an unselfish role Kovalevskiy played in her married life. This was due, in one way or another, to his enthusiasm for the trends of the day in society. Abroad, his wife was studying mathematics, and he natural sciences. I believe they lived abroad for five years, and he was to rest from the pressures of his publishing activities; unfortunately, he took from her the not entirely correct idea that one could do great things even with small means. The fruit of this thought was a period of housebuilding in Petersburg which ended in bankruptcy. One cannot say that he, a poor dreamer and impractical man, endured this time. He finally came to the quiet refuge of a professorship, but it was already too late—he had effervesced too much in life.

Kovalevskiy did not belong to Botkin's circle. I became acquainted with him at the beginning of his publishing activities, when my future wife—my unfailing friend until death—and I became occupied with translations, which began in 1863.

Entrance to the Medical Academy was closed for women this year, and both of my female students, continuing to burn with the desire to live by independent work and to serve mankind, were almost doomed to life in the Kirghiz steppes. The difficulty was that at that time the authorities of the Orenburg territory had already announced the desirability of having women doctors for the Mohammedan population in view of the fact that Mohammedan women stubbornly shunned the help of male doctors. Having heard about this, both the young enthusiasts decided to give the authorities a signed statement that they would go to the steppe only if they were allowed to study at the academy. At this time they already had their certificates showing they had passed the examination for the boys' gymnasium course. I did not have the common sense to understand that the two young women, going to the wild steppe with its million and one-half population, were condemning themselves to ruination without material benefit, and I gave the memorandum to the then Director of the War Ministry Office (later Turkestan governor), Kaufman. Fortunately, no answer came from this note, and my friends were saved from the misfortune threatening them. I say this seriously because knowing their thoughts and frame of mind, I am sure they would have set off for the steppe once they had given their formal promise. A year later, one of them went abroad to study medicine, while the other stayed home and worked on translations since she had a well-rounded education, knew languages, and could write in Russian.

Yesterday, when I first touched upon this important point in my life, I began to remember everything that this translator was for me right up to the grave, I turned this over in my mind during the night, and this morning I am doing her portrait quietly, without the least adornment or exaggeration.

In work she was not only a comrade, but also an example. On her estate was a horse named Komar, remarkable for the fact that in harness, without any urging, as if from a feeling of accepting duties for himself, he held the traces always drawn taut and in case of need pulled with all his might, never tiring of working for others. This was the way of Mariya Aleksandrovna in all her occupations—in translations as well as in matters of the country farm. As Komar carried out his work neatly, so did Mariya Aleksandrovna. Her translations did not require outside editing; she received her estate in a state of disorder and repaired it so that it was considered one of the model estates in the district. For the latter, however, she was indebted not only to her own diligence, but to still one more trait of her character; she did not put up with lapses in anything—not in her dress, nor in her form, nor in her life; as soon as they appeared, she would try not to let them grow into holes, and repaired them immediately (she was a dressmaker both in the figurative and in the actual sense of the word). There were instances in her life in which the closing up of gaps which, as usual, did not happen through any fault of her own, demanded long and agonizing efforts, but nevertheless she darned, darned, and the gap was closed. A disinterested person by nature, and a neat worker who abandoned herself to her business, she thought little about the external adornments of life for herself but, as far as her means allowed, she loved to supply them to those close around her who were made happy by them. The only luxury she allowed herself was books, artistic albums, from time to time the theater or concerts, and still less often a trip abroad to Italy, which she loved most of all. Behind this aspect of an active, intelligent and educated woman worker stood a woman who knew how to master herself, with a fiery heart capable of energetic good. At the end of her studies and during the last stages of the Franco-Prussian War, a party of medical people under the leadership of the professor of surgery, Rose, went from Zurich to France, in the neighborhood of Belfort, and she went with them as a sister of mercy. All the dirty work around the unfortunate remnants of Bourbak's army fell to her share, in mud, rags, with frostbitten feet. She bore the ordeal to the end. And even at her own place in the country she was not squeamish later with the peasants' infirmities, and she helped them during the years so seriously and skillfully that she earned the confidence of the population and received thanks from the district council. For those close to her she was constantly a careful nurse—this was almost the main trait in the serious side of her nature. However, she looked upon those close to her with wide open eyes and most of all did not stand for lies and falsity. She inherited honor to the point of punctiliousness from her father, a strict, very educated general.

In such a way there were in her nature all the conditions for giving an intimate person, who could distinguish gold from tinsel, happiness in youth, at a mature age, and in old age.

Among the events of 1864 the following occurrence is engraved in my memory.

In Lithuania, among the Polish insurgents taken prisoner was the second lieutenant in the Russian service, Malevich (or Malevskiy, I do not remember). He had received bruises on his head during the encounters and was taken to Vilna in a state of unconsciousness. By Murav'yev's order he was subjected to a whole series of tests in the hospital for pretense, and when the tests did not give a clear answer, the results were sent by Murav'yev to the Medical Academy for examination and a conclusion. The academy entrusted the examination of the whole affair to Balinskiy, Botkin and me.

According to the register of experiments supplied us, the experiments consisted of the following. Behind the door of the room where the sick man lay, doctors' assistants took turns watching the patient day and night through a small opening in the door. The sick man did not ask to eat, and was not fed. He did not urinate and was not catheterized for three days so that the bladder was stretched to the navel. The patient was unexpectedly doused with ice water, huddled himself up shivering, but did not let go. A needle was placed under the upper lid of his closed eyes and the surface of the eye tickled with it—he spasmodically screwed up his eyes, tears flowed, but he did not let go. Melted sealing wax was dropped on his bare body—he pulled his hand back, but he did not let go.

Not satisfied with this, Murav'yev wrote from Königsberg to Burov, a local professor of surgery, for a consultation with the hospital doctor. Burov considered that the question could only be solved by trepanation of the skull in the place of the contusion.

I do not know why our renowned State man, who was even honored with a memorial in Vilna, did not solve this problem. Neither do I know what significance he gave our decision and whether God sent death to the patient, Malevich, in the hospital or whether he got well and was moved when he had convalesced.

During the years 1863-1867, my pupil and I translated Hermann's textbook of physiology and Kühne's textbook of physiological chemistry. I wrote *Physiology of the Nervous System* (Petersburg, 1866) in three installments, and worked sometimes alone and sometimes with my students (Matkevich, Pashutin, Voroshilov, Tarkhanov, Litvinov and Spiro) exclusively on the nervous system of the frog. The only exception was Voroshilov's work on the nitrogen exchange in the body with use of leguminous plants for food. The following pertained to me personally during this time: the analysis of Brown-Séquard's phenomenon, the topography of the spinal centers of the frog's front extremities, the intercentral connections between the spinal centers of the front and back legs, localization of the collective centers for the extremities of the frog in the cerebrum and their relation to the reflexes between the front and back legs.

These experiments were published at the time in German journals and were described in detail in my *Physiology of the Nervous System,* in chapters III and IV. The following was said in the preface to this book: "I was prompted to write the physiology of the nervous system principally by the circumstance that in all, even the best textbooks of physiology, a purely anatomical principle is taken as a basis of particular description of nerve phenomena . . ., from the very first year of teaching the physiology of the nervous system, I began following another way, that is, I described in lectures the acts as they happen in reality. This endeavor succeeded, and now I am presenting the attempt to the public for judgment in the form of a book." I believe even now that I was right in describing nerve phenomena specifically as they were described in this book.

In the spring of 1863 I went, with my whole company, to my relatives in Simbirsk province. Those who went with me were: a most delightful old German lady, Anna Khristianovna; my sister's husband's aunt, who was leaving Petersburg for the second time in her life; one from the institute who had just finished the course and was charged to her; a physician-surgeon who had just finished the course and was called to spend the summer in practice in the country; and a big black Newfoundland, Druzhok, whom I was taking as a gift to my brother Andrey, a great lover of dogs. In Tver' we took a steamship and went down the Volga to Vasil'sursk. To the delight of Anna Khristianovna, it was not the end, and even I feasted my eyes upon the beauties of the Volga in the Kostroma province for the first time. A young surgeon, a student in the fifth year who came with me and lodged in our home, became famous for successfully removing the arm and shoulder blade of a sick person.

In our out-of-the-way place, there was no surgeon near at hand, and he had hardly appeared and begun his practice when masses of people began to throng to him. He was of excessive daring; in spite of the fact that he had just left the school bench he undertook everything. He removed a cataract from one old landowner; he excised a pile for my brother and performed an operation on a fistula for him; he sucessfully performed two lithotomies, burned through and cut several tumors and, encouraged by his successes, went to extremes to the point where he decided on the following reckless experiment (I found out about this only after the experiment was done, or I would have dissuaded him from it, of course). The sexton's wife came to him with an enormous stomach. Whether he did a trial puncture on her or not I do not know, but in any case he acted recklessly, injecting iodine brandy into her stomach as if he were dealing with an edematous testicle. The poor woman writhed for a week from torment and left with the same stomach with which she had come.

He was not compassionate. My niece's young governess had a wart on her finger and, of course, wanted to get rid of it. To his warning that it would be painful, she bravely answered that she would bear it, and she really did bear it with tears in her eyes when he passed two pins crosswise under the base of the wart and pulled the pins through with a thread. Be that as it may, he did much good.

I lived in the country during the summer of 1864, on the shore of the Neva, and I began to write *The Physiology of the Nervous System*. In my spare moments I studied the compound eyes of insects (the huge eyes of the dragon-fly), but I did not find anything new. I saw only how insignificantly the conjugate foci of the corneal facets are changed with considerable changes of distances of objects from the eye and the absolute invariability of the curvature of the compound eye's whole surface during electrical stimulation.

During vacation of the following year (1865), my wife and I went abroad, via Switzerland, to Italy. We left in the beginning of spring, when the trees had just begun to turn green. Germany was in bloom; on the top of St. Gothard Pass on May 17 there was a snowstorm, but a few hours beyond the pass the wheat was already ripe, and on Lago di Como we ate delicious cherries. We were, of course, also on Lago Maggiore, and then from Genoa we went by sea to Naples. I remember that when we were in Civitavecchia, there were three German tourists going from Rome to Naples on the ship. One of them, a healthy, thick-set man with a bouquet of flowers in his button-hole, evidently a leader among his comrades, began to orate with great anima-tion about the wonders of Rome as soon as he had boarded ship. But the ship had hardly left the harbor and begun to rock when it became impossible not to notice that although he stood firm, his tone began to weaken, and his speech stopped suddenly, and he sat near the side which was at the service of those who could not endure the tossing. My poor wife suffered cruelly from seasick-ness and spent almost all of the trip in bed. From our ride about the environs of Naples, I remember especially our ascent of Vesuvius.

From Portici we went on horseback almost to the base of the ash cone. Here guides attached themselves to us offering services, but M. A. decisively turned down their help. The day was sunny and hot, and I remember that we rested after every five steps, sticking our feet in the ashes. She endured this torment without outside help, climbing, I think, a whole hour. At this time, Vesuvius fired every minute, throwing out a column of smoke and rocks. We had the opportunity to go up to the very edge of an old crater and see the formation on it of two new cones, from which the rocks and smoke were flying. We ran from the summit to the foot of the cone in about ten minutes. Of course, we also went to the Blue Grotto on Capri. From Naples, we moved to Sorrento for the remainder of the summer. We lived, of course, very quietly, working —I at nerve physiology, my wife at translations. We went boating on the sea, we went on donkeys about the environs, and that was all. For the whole summer in Sorrento there were two noisy holidays: a celebration in honor of the local madonna, and the national celebration of freeing Naples from the Bourbons. The celebration in honor of the madonna consisted of the uninterrupted shooting of petards during a church service; after Mass an image of the madonna was carried outside and placed in a recess in the wall of the church. After it appeared, a chorus of musicians standing in front of the madonna began to serenade her, but not in the form of some church cantata, but with gay arias. The other holiday, or at least part of it, took place on the town square, where portraits of Victor Emmanuel and Garibaldi were brought. A chorus of musicians played Garibaldi's anthem, and the audience began to echo it with hundreds of voices. When this was over, there was a thunder of applause.

I remember even now from life in Sorrento the orange orchard around the house (villa Grehan) in which we lived, and its terrace on which two very young men appeared one fine day to make our acquaintance. These were the future pride of Russia—Il'ya Il'ich Mechnikov and Aleksandr Onufriyevich Kovalevskiy. I remember that I had just then finished writing the innervation of respiratory movements, and for that reason I read this passage to them. I often saw both of them then, and I will have more opportunity to speak about them, but at that time our acquaintance continued for only a few days. On the way back to Russia, we stopped in Rome and in Florence.

Occupation with writing and working on the nervous system required three years of time, including in the laboratory over the cellar (which I did not know), and this so impaired my health that I began to imagine heavens knows what with the over-anxiety characteristic of me. I began to accustom myself to the thought that I would probably have to give up my professorship since I did not want to occupy the position with red ears. I even mentally selected a successor for myself in the person of one young man who at that time had published two very good works abroad, who, however, I did not know personally. Fate, as if on purpose, gave me a chance to become acquainted with him upon his return to his native land via Petersburg. The thought about him as a successor was abandoned, there was not another suitable one present, and I tried to cure myself with rest and waters, according to Botkin's advice. I had enough money from the sale of my publications, and I received a year's leave abroad in the spring of 1867.

I spent the beginning of the summer in Karlsbad, and got well, thanks to long daily walks in the air and went to Harz to an old friend, Rollet, who was a professor there. My former pupil Suslova, who had just finished her studies in Zurich, had just arrived there with the purpose of working on her doctor's thesis with my assistance. The topic given to her was such that she could work in her own apartment and was exactly a question for delicate feminine hands —over tiny frog lymph hearts. She obtained very good results, established clearly a series of analogies between the neural apparatus of the hearts and the reflex cutaneous-muscle mechanisms; namely, the excitability of the stopped hearts from the skin and their diastolic stopping with the same stimulation of the central part of the cerebrum which evokes inhibition of spinal reflexes. As a witness to these experiments, I tested the influence of this stimulation on the heart and received a diastolic stopping of the heart. This means that with stimulation of the optic lobes, three effects occurred simultaneously: inhibition of reflexes, inhibition of heart activity and inhibition of the activity of the four lymph hearts. I know that Ad. Fik, at that time professor of physiology in Zurich, approved very much of this dissertation. It was translated into Russian. In the beginning of 1868, M. A. came to visit me, and in the spring she went to Zurich to finish studying medicine.

For my part, I did not sit with folded arms either.

Among the critics of my work on inhibition of reflexes, the most resolute was the student G. Schiff. Not denying the correctness of my facts, he maintained, on the basis of his own experiments, that there were no such arresting mechanisms here, and the matter was explained very simply by the fact that when the nervous system is strongly shocked it of course ceases to respond to weak stimulation of the skin—from a strong blow on the head both animal and man lose consciousness, sensitivity and mobility. This objection was incorrect in principle: the chemical stimulation of cross sections of the brain which I used was not so strong as to produce paralysis of sensitivity; applied to the hemispheres, it did not produce any effect, and in parts near the medulla it evoked signs of pain and escape of the animal, as from fear. But in his experiments with strong stimulation (which were very crude in method) of nerve trunks, there were hints that inhibition of reflexes could be evoked also by this means. Incidentally, systematic experiments with stimulation of sensory nerves did not exist, and I decided to take them up. The work, done and published in Graz,[14] turned out to be extremely gratifying. Reflex centers of the spine (on frogs with destroyed brains) and locomotor centers of the cerebrum (on animals with hemispheres removed) were excited from the sensory nerve simultaneously. The latter turned out to be more sensitive in general. The separate induction shocks, even the strong ones, gave only individual flinches, but series even of weak ones, produced coordinated movements;

[14] Ueber d. elektr. u chem. Reiz d. sensibl. Rückenmarksnerven d. Frosch., Graz, 1868.

other things being equal, the latter came easier the closer the series of shocks or the more each of them was prolonged. Tetanization of the nerves evoked two effects: coordinated movements and a depressed state of the nerve centers; under weak tetanization, movement predominated, under strong, depression; stopping the tetanization instantly provoked strong movements.

Chemical stimulation of the nerves produced in essence the same thing as weak and strong tetanization. A depressed state of nerve centers with chemical stimulation of the nerve resulted in the following form of the experiment: the frog with hemispheres cut out endured motionlessly (in a free position) chemical stimulation of the nerve with sodium chloride during 3 to 4 minutes. At this time, inhibition developed so strongly that even a strong pinching of the feet did not provoke movements; as soon as the stimulated end of the nerve was cut off, however, the animal gave a jump, sometimes even shrieking, and the sensitivity of the feet was instantly restored.[15]

On my return to Russia in the winter of 1868, I gave public lectures at the "Art Club," and Ivan Sergeyevich Turgenev came to one of them. The seat beside the chair was set aside for him as guest of honor. I lectured on spatial phenomena on that evening and, when I got to the influence of the degree of the eyes' contraction on the apparent size of objects—a fact apparent only in a stereoscope on moving the stereograms in and out—Ivan Sergeyevich was so obliging that he agreed to certify the correctness of the fact before the audience. Standing on the chair and looking into Wheatstone's mirror stereoscope, he announced in a loud voice that he really saw a change in the size of the images in the said direction.

My polemics with Konstantin Dmitriyevich Kavelin apropos of his book *Problems of Psychology* probably date from this or the following year. I wrote "Notes" for this book, not knowing Konstantin Dmitriyevich personnally nor his noble way of thinking, nor his merits as a scholar. Knowing all this, I would not have written my own "notes," and of course would have limited myself to my latest article, "Who must investigate the problems of psychology, and how?" because all the important objections raised against the basic propositions of the book, making a direct analysis of them as unwarranted, were indirectly included in it. I tell this because it was very unpleasant for me

---

[15] Apropos of this experiment, I automatically recall Rollet's closest friends—Tomashek, a professor of German literature, and Pöbal, a professor of chemistry, with whom I kept company and who sometimes visited the laboratory. Pöbal was a great joker and once, as a witness of the experiment just described, he remarked: "After this, just how can one not believe children when they contend that one can catch a sparrow by putting salt on his tail." In this experiment, the frog was placed with his entire leg crossed under him, and in place of the other, the prepared nerve, the end of which was salted, stuck out from his body like a thin tail. This poor joker was tragically killed after several years. A former laboratory assistant cut his throat one afternoon in the street in revenge for Pöbal's having dismissed him for carelessness and drunkenness.

to think about my "notes" when I became acquainted with Konstantin Dmitri-yevich personally and found in him a man who regarded me from the very first meeting in a most friendly way. On this—fortunately the only such occa-sion of my life—I deviated from a rule which Ludwig followed and which I knew from his words: "Answer an attack not otherwise than by a deed." In Konstantin Dmitriyevich's book there were important attacks on my psycho-logical beliefs, and I went to extremes for the first and last time in my life.

During these years, my former illness, general weakness with dizziness, returned, not disposing me either to activity or to a cheerful mood. The aca-demic years 1868 and 1869 were the most unproductive ones in my life and, perhaps, thanks to this, I regarded the state of affairs in the Academy more gloomily (perhaps even not entirely justly) than I should have. This mood came to an end in 1870 with my leaving the Academy, and I consider it of some use to dwell on the incentives which brought me to such a finale.

In raising stock for the maintenance of a certain breed, it is recognized as necessary to renew the blood from time to time by the introduction of outside elements into the breed or "the breed of relations from generation to genera-tion" will degenerate. There is no doubt that we will apply this law also to great groups of people who have been compelled during a very long period to become related among themselves. In what measure the same law can be car-ried over into the intellectual sphere of people living from generation to gener-ation, with just the same interests and following set rules and tastes in their group, I will not undertake to determine, but I believe that here also the intro-duction into a circle of members with rather different views and tastes would be more useful than harmful, counteracting the formation of a routine in the circle, i.e., its stagnation. From this point of view the manner adopted by the German universities of inviting to their midst foreigners of higher worth than their own pupils is considered in all fairness, I believe, a rule supporting the well being of the universities. From the same point of view, the establish-ment of a professors' boarding school at the Medical Academy before we (Botkin, Bekkers and myself) entered always seemed to me an unfair act regarding the Russian universities and one capable of harming even the Acad-emy itself. According to the regulations of this institution, ten pupils selected from the Academy who had finished the course always stayed in it, and two of them each year went abroad for advanced training in the sciences after two years of advanced training in them at the boarding school.

In just what university are ten people retained by such rules in only one medical department, and also, is it possible to maintain that each year only two pupils of the academy are worthy, according to their work, of being sent abroad, but in the other medical departments time is not passed in the same way? If one takes into account that the trip abroad very often—I believe for more than half of those sent—finishes with a professorship, then it becomes clear that as soon as a position in the Academy is open, the closest candidate for it would be a pupil from the boarding school. The authorities and the professors know him, and he is their man. But teachers often love their pupils as their own, and the pupil of the boarding school who had become a professor would regard a pupil of the same boarding school as a candidate for a chair, like a schoolfellow. All this would be in the order of things. But does the Academy gain from this? In 1870, five new professors from the boarding school joined it; of these, one was really a very capable man, but the other four were perhaps people who knew their work, but in no way contributed to the renown of the Academy. Mr. Delyanov's ill-fated university regulations were not yet in existence at that time, and in the universities, lectures of the favorite professors still continued to be visited not by the students of their respective departments alone, and friendly contact among students of different departments was still unrestricted. It was this way in my student days, and I knew of more than one example of much that was good coming to the mind of a medical student from other departments. He who knew how to make use of this blessing of university life obviously had chances of leaving the university a better educated person than his comrades who had fed five years on medicine alone. I frankly confess that I considered the pupils of the academy deprived of one of the existent boons of university life, and that privilege which they used seemed to me more unfair. I have not kept these thoughts about the professors' boarding school secret, and of course I have not stirred up good feelings towards myself as far as the authorities are concerned, or the former boarding school pupils or professors, who have considered it a blessing for the academy. Those students who were reckoning on the boarding school, of course, could not like them.

In answer to my advice not to enter the boarding school at the end of the course but to go directly abroad at his father's expense, I received even a fierce, abusive letter from one of my pupils who later attained certain degrees. In such a way, by my own fault, I was not one of the favorites in the professors' midst (with the exception, of course, of Botkin and Gruber; we seldom saw each other) and I of course felt this, but continued to stagnate. I further acknowledge that the change of tone in the upper echelons of the Academy since Dubovitskiy, who was truly benevolent to the Academy, passed away, when kind old Naranovich, who had temporarily substituted for him, left, and N. N. Zinin left the Academy, was not at all to my taste. In such circumstances, in the fall of 1870, there were to be elections of two professors—for the zoology department, with the old academician Brandt's departure, and for the histology chair, again open. There were two candidates for both chairs in my subject. I. I. Mechnikov, who at that time was already a big name in

zoology, could not join Petersburg University for lack of a professorial position there, and he left for Odessa as a professor, but continued to be drawn
towards Petersburg, and exchanging letters with me, he willingly agreed to
take Brandt's place. Concerning the second candidate, it is first of all necessary to remark that in those early times there were no medical-histologists in
Russia,[16] and as such I knew only one, A. Ye. Golubev, who had worked at
the same time with me in Rollet's laboratory, who was greatly carried away
with histology (Rollet, as a pupil of Brücke, was half histologist), and did
before my eyes, completely independently, very good work with the influence
of electrical stimulation on the capillary walls. Besides that, I knew that Rollet
valued him very much as a skillful and careful (even too strict) worker.

And so when the elections came, I, according to the regulations of the Academy, had the right to propose—and I did propose—both candidates. It would
be ridiculous to compare the man proposed against Mechnikov with the latter,
according to his merits in science, and the opposing party knew how to avoid
this, as we shall see. Concerning the histologist proposed by the opposing side
(their comrade in the Academy), his histological work was more important
than that of my candidate, but it came from Ludwig's laboratory to press
under the general name of Ludwig and their candidate, and besides, it was on
one of the questions most interesting to Ludwig—about the structure of the
kidney—since in his life he was occupied a great deal with the investigation
of the analysis of urine. I put this forward as an argument against the independent work of their candidate. Unfortunately, I had forgotten then about
Ludwig's letter to me which he wrote in November 1863 where he talked
about this work,[17] and I could bring in a counter argument only in a general
form. For this they remarked to me, not without malevolence, that I, as a
man who had not studied histology, could hardly be a competent judge of
histological work and of the question as to what in a given case, belongs to
one or another investigation. The important thing was, they said, that the

---

[16] This is not taking Yakubovich and Ovsyannikov into account: one was a professor of
physiology, and the other a member of the Academy of Sciences. There may have been
histologists in Dorpat, but we never heard about any.

[17] Now, looking over my old correspondence, I found this letter of Ludwig and am
extracting from it everything concerning this problem, word for word. "Mit der Nieren-
anatomie bin ich, nur soweit es das Schwein betrifft, im Reinen und ich werde ihnen,
wenn die Abhandlung gedruckt ist, Nachricht geben. Wenn ich wüsste, wo Z. (their
candidate) steckte, von dem ich seit seiner Abreise nichts weiter gehört habe, so würde
ich ihm wissen lassen inwiefern das, was unter seinem und meinem Namen gedruckt wird,
von dem abweicht, was wir schon gemeinsam herausgebracht. [With respect to the
anatomy of the kidney, as far as the matter concerns the pig, everything is cleared up for
me, and I will advise you when the article is printed. If I knew where Z. (their candidate) was, about whom I have heard nothing more since he left, then I would have let
him know to what extent that which will be printed under his and my name differs from
what I discovered earlier together with him]. . . . The original of the letter will be kept
in my papers.

work was signed by our candidate, meaning that he took part in the work and in the results. In this way, my first candidate was turned down. Before the balloting, one of the old men did not refrain from saying: "Why do we need a stranger when there is one of our own." And when it was time to ballot for Mechnikov, one of the professors got up and said the following: "According to his scientific merits Mechnikov is worthy of being not only a professor in our Academy, but even a member of the Academy of Sciences. We can invite him only as an ordinarius professor, but why should we have an ordinarius professor for a secondary chair in the Academy when there is still in prospect substitution of such important chairs for cutaneous, syphilitic, and ear disorders. An extraordinarius man is sufficient for us for this place; therefore, I place a black ball for Mechnikov." The majority followed this conviction, Mechnikov was turned down, and on the very same day or the next I sent in my resignation from the Academy. They of course did not ask me to stay. And this would have been useless. Soon then, by Mechnikov's endeavors, I was chosen for Odessa University, but the choice was not confirmed (as I have said above) by Mr. Delyanov until the spring of the following year. During these months I went to Dmitriy Ivanovich Mendeleyev's laboratory; he gave me a topic, telling me how to prepare the substance, nitrous methyl ether, and what to do with it; he gave me a room, utensils, materials, and I with great pleasure set to work, the more so since I had not had in my hands before this, substances which boiled at low temperatures, and this boiled at a $-12°$. Dmitriy Ivanovich himself described the results of this apprentice work. To be a pupil of such a teacher as Mendeleyev was of course both pleasant and useful, but I had already partaken of too much physiology to be disloyal to it, and I did not become a chemist.

I know for sure that Countess Shuvalov, the first wife of the former, later minister to Berlin, took trouble about my approval in Odessa, which did not come for a long time, without my knowledge. S. P. Botkin treated this family and was on friendly terms with it. Through him the Countess (I did not know her personally, but I heard a great deal about her, of her high, sincere qualities) found out about my affair and strongly attacked Ivan Davydovich, but he did not yield. I learned all this from Sergey Petrovich already after the unsuccessful attack. A little later I was presented the opportunity of securing a yet stronger voice on my behalf, but I did not want to use this. In my academy laboratory, in the last year of my stay there, a very nice and a very poor student, Drozdov, son of the village priest in an out-of-the-way place in the Vologod province,[18] worked there. This Drozdov was very distressed about the fate of his only sister, growing up, a girl who was very intelligent and capable,

---

[18] He made a very interesting observation—the disappearance of the white blood corpuscles from the frog's blood with curare poisoning.

in his words, but deprived of all means for an education in the backwoods. He and I thought about ways to relieve his grief, and finally we found a way. I asked a friend in the Academy, Professor Eichwald, to intercede about this; the matter was taken care of, and the girl was admitted in an institute after I had already left the Academy. Eichwald solicited in my name, and thus I had to thank a high person for the kind attention given to my request. I went with the sole thought of thanking him, and my first words were, of course, an expression of gratitude, but then they asked me about the German professors with whom I studied, especially about Brücke; they remarked in passing that I had published *Reflexes of the Brain* in vain, to which I answered (the conversation took place in German) : "Man muss doch die Courage haben seine Ueberzeugungen auszudrücken."[19] But in conclusion I was asked whether I knew Mr. Delyanov personally, and in what state was the question about my move to Odessa. Of course, these people high up were accustomed to having people come to them very often with requests, if not in their pockets, then in their souls, and this question was probably asked with a benevolent purpose —to facilitate bringing out on the surface the request kept secret in my soul. But it did not even cross my mind to ask about receiving the position, and to this question I answered: "Ich gedenke mich in dieser Angelegenheit ganz neutral zu verhalten."[20]

The meeting ended with this. I have already told above that my approval finally went through, and in just what form.

About life in Odessa, this nice half-European city, I have preserved my most pleasant recollections of these times.

[19] One must nevertheless have the courage to express his convictions.
[20] In this matter I intend to conduct myself entirely neutrally.

7

PROFESSORSHIP IN ODESSA UNIVERSITY (1870-1876)

WHEN I moved to Odessa I decided to study absorptiometrically the question of the state of CO_2 in the blood; therefore, the first task was to set up an absorptiometer according to the plan already known from the former description and a series of accessory contrivances from glass which were necessary for such experiments. Fortunately, there was a mechanic at the university who could prepare, according to my instructions, the metal parts of the apparatus, but I had to manage with the glass myself since there was no glassblower in Odessa; I had some understanding of this skill[1] and knew how to make tubes. The premises I received for a laboratory were very good, but not at all adapted for the work; therefore, I had to take a great deal of trouble in this direction. I cannot help recollecting about this with gratitude concerning the friendly kindness of the chemistry professor A. A. Verigo, who did me a great service in the detailed organization of the laboratory. I was very cordially received by all my new colleagues; but at this time my only close friend, I. I. Mechnikov, was not there, but was on a year's leave, and two of the other distinguished scholars, the chemist, N. N. Sokolov and the botanist Tsenskovskiy, left the university, and I could not become close friends with them. Therefore, during the first year of my stay at Odessa, my company was composed of:

---

[1] When I was already a professor in the Medical Academy, on one of my trips to Berlin I took lessons in blowing from a glassblower there, Geissler, who was filled with the importance of the subject he taught, and for this reason took a Friedrichsdor (more than 5 rubles) from me for the lesson. I paid dearly for the study, but in return I was enabled to work at Odessa.

A. A. Verigo, a very original and kind keeper of Vidhalm's zoological museum, and my assistant, P. A. Spiro, who came with me to Odessa from the Medical Academy—he was a student there, and here he became an assistant. At the Medical Academy all my students usually worked in the same room with me, and at work all of us who could sing often sang in a chorus, since our laboratory stood by itself and our singing did not infringe on the good name of the educational institution. Among us, as singers, Spiro was recognized as the most talented; but his singing talents were revealed only in Odessa, when he obtained a government apartment—a room almost the size of a dancing hall, with excellent resonance—and he provided himself with an instrument. Not having gone through any school, he sang, moreover, in such a way that he could evoke tears (I was a witness to this); he sang with an Italian manner and mimicked Tamberlik. He, poor fellow, missed his real road, and it was already too late now to turn to it—he had neglected the talent given to him by God too long. Later in the spring of 1871 my wife defended her doctoral thesis in Zurich, and I went to Switzerland to celebrate her finishing her course. Wishing to afford pleasure in gaieties to her girl-friend in the university, then still a student, Miss Ioker, she invited her to take a trip around Switzerland, and we three left via Ragaz [where, of course, we did not fail to admire the wild canyon Tamina (Taminaschlucht, along the via mola)]. From the summit halt Ioker headed back, and we went to Italy, boarded in Genoa a small abominable steamer with the high-flown name of Risorgimento[2] which went between this city and Spezia almost without ballast and we rocked along the calm sea for eight hours to Spezia, and from here by boat to the hamlet of San Terenzo on the seashore. We settled there near that historic home where Byron and Shelley, who drowned in the bay of San Terenzo, had lived. There was not yet a railroad along the seashore between Genoa and Spezia, or else we would have been in three delightful places, which comprise the now so-called Italian Riviera, and where I was with my wife in the spring of 1903. But, as I have said, the Italian Riviera at that time did not exist; we went to unpretentious, cheap San Terenzo to enjoy the sea; it was at our feet, and we really did enjoy it, passing a month and a half there. We lived, of course, very quietly, worked on translations, bathed, and took walks around the environs. On the way back we stopped in Florence, Venice, and Vienna. In the last town we parted: my wife went to Petersburg to take her examinations for the right to practice (she received this right in December 1871), and I went to Odessa. For Christmas this year I was in Petersburg. Here we became acquainted with the ophthalmologist Ivanov, a professor at Kiev University, who offered M.A. an assistantship in his clinic. She, however, intended

---

[2] The name for the period of Italian wars of independence in the nineteenth century. *Translator*

to go to Vienna to finish studying, and left for there in January 1872.

I have already told how I passed the winter of 1871. The following year I began forming the real circle of friends, because of which I love Odessa even in these times. I. I. Mechnikov returned from abroad. A still very young man, N. A. Umov, who had made a great impression by his opening lecture, came from Moscow to the chair of mathematical physics. Another Muscovite, Duvernoit, came into the chair of Roman law, and he gave a fascinating introductory lecture. And still after a year Umov brought to Odessa his young wife, my future, kind, good friend, and the circle was a complete set— it constituted the nucleus which Kandakov and his wife later joined. Yelena Leonardovna Umova at that time had the appearance of a young girl with two of the most winning traits of unspoiled youth—sincerity and impulsiveness. In her new place, she now wept about abandoning Moscow, now shone and was glad for the present, and for a husband God gave her a good, considerate and loving man who knew how to comfort his "Lenochka"[3] in her naïve sorrows. For a friendly circle of workers, a family home was just as indispensable as a warm comfortable corner for a tired person. Only in a family home with the friendly smile and affectionate word of the hostess does a meeting of friends rest emotionally and assume that character of respectability and cordiality which the Germans express by the word Gemütlichkeit. The Umov's apart-ment became such a connecting group-salon of the circle. The host, besides his refined amiability, turned out to be inveterately hospitable; the hostess pre-sented an element of cordiality; I had the importance of a not entirely aged uncle, but the life of the circle was I. I. Mechnikov. Of all the young people I have known, I have never in my life met a more fascinating person than Il'ya Il'ich, by the liveliness of his mind, his inexhaustible wit and his well-rounded education. He was so serious and productive in science—at that time he had already done a great deal in zoology and had made a great name for himself in it—so alive, entertaining and so varied in friendly company. One of the delights of the circle was his ability to cleverly notice the comic side in current events and the droll features in the character of personages, with an astonish-ing ability to imitate their voices, movements, and manner of speaking. Who of us Odessanites of that time can forget, for example, the image of the lame astronomer which he portrayed, how he in a dressing gown and nightcap looks through the open window of his bedroom at the starry sky, in such a way making astronomical observations; or the botanist with the peacock voice, who calls out with animation and pride a long series of foreign names of vegetable pigments; or, finally, the cheeping of a certain small, downtrodden subinspec-tor who, at any new acquaintance, introduced himself as the nephew of a general-field store master in the Austrian service. Mechnikov did all this

---

[3] An affectionate diminutive for Yelena. *Translator*

without the least malice; he was not in the least a scoffer. And even his heart, in relation to his close ones, stood on a level with his talents—without any collateral means, with only his salary as a professor, he took his first, sick, wife to Madeira, thinking to save her, and he denied himself a great deal during this time, and never uttered a single word about this. He was a great lover of music and could sing many classical things; he loved the theater, but did not like to go to a tragedy because he sobbed irrepressibly.

I had met Aleksandr Onufriyevich Kovalevskiy, our famous zoologist, two times cursorily before he left Kiev for Odessa: in Sorrento (as I have already told above), and in Petersburg, in my laboratory at the Medical Academy. He came here to solve two problems: how do the nerves of a crayfish react to stimulation in an electro-motor relation, and does the nerve chain of the crayfish pass the stimulation along its length. For these goals he was given a galvanometer, and in the course of two or three sittings he could satisfy himself from his own experiments that in the first regard there was no difference between crayfish and frog nerves and that a break of the chain with knots does not hinder the spread of tetanic effect along its length, i.e., the negative fluctuation of the current. He came to Odessa I believe a year before I returned from there to Petersburg. Later he became a member of our circle, but the first year, since he was a family man and a little morose, he did not take up with our company at once; therefore, I did not succeed in knowing him as a member of the circle, but I did succeed in knowing and valuing him as a professor. His opening lecture was very original. During the first years of my stay a very intelligent and honored archpriest, who did not intervene in university matters, lived the rest of his days in the position of professor of theology at the university. He left his post in old age, and in his place came a young clergyman who must have understood his appointment as having to watch over the teaching of the sciences in the university, that is, how far they conformed to Orthodoxy. With such thoughts in his mind, he of course did not fail to visit the new professor A. O. Kovalevskiy's introductory lecture, to become acquainted with his way of thinking. To crown his embarrassment, the new professor at the lecture turned out to be a heretic—a confirmed Darwinist. Our father bristled up and, in the words of Professor Bogdanovskiy, contemplated sending the Minister a thunderous denunciation of the lecturer and his studies; with difficulty they persuaded him that all zoology was so contaminated with Darwinian heresy that it was impossible to find it free from the above-mentioned. It is known that Aleksandr Onufriyevich as a worker-investigator possessed extraordinary energy, and he was probably the same as a teacher, judging by what I saw. There was no chair of histology in Odessa University, and Aleksandr Onufriyevich, who was a specialist in the history of growth, was by necessity the histologist. And what did he do? On his own initiative, without any obligation to teach histology, he put his listeners to work with the microscope and began to teach them microscopy. I appreciated how seriously he regarded this matter. The room where he gave the course on histology was just over my laboratory, and I, for some trifling matter, went up to him. I came, at a table with microscopes sat the students, and he walked about the room silently and with a serious face; I approached him freely, in a friendly way; but I had not succeeded in getting a word out when he apologized in a very serious way that unfortunately he was busy and could not enter into conversation. I must observe that he did not consider me light-minded, not worthy of a person's attention, and was disposed to me in a most friendly way.

I liked Professor Duvernoit very much as an intelligent, extremely courteous, good, honorable man; he was a frequent guest of ours, not being a habitué of the circle. I cannot but mention with a good word three more professors: Golovinskiy, a well-known geologist, and two very learned eccentrics, Slavist Grigorovich and an archeologist. These two were unworldly, especially Grigorovich, who considered almost the chief business of his life the fact that he had succeeded in stealing some very important manuscript in one of the Afonskiy monasteries and publishing it. In Odessa he became famous for being able to recommend his own really deserving candidate for an open chair in such a way that not his candidate, but another—a person bearing the same surname as the latter—got it.

Our circle constituted a party in the University only in the following respect: we did not seek the post of either dean or rector, did not try to place our relatives in the University and did not go either with complaints or requests about patronage to a trustee, which many in the University did. Alas! There was amidst the professors even such a man who made a denunciation to the local censor (an out-councillor whose name I do not remember) of his own colleague, the editor of the University transactions, that he had falsified the records of the conferences. I was at the council meetings when Professor Pavlov of canon law, accused of falsification, publicly and in a loud voice in the presence of the informer said: "Mr. . . . has informed against me to the censor (such-and-such a name) that I falsify the proceedings of conferences; therefore, I ask that an investigation be set. . . ." The informer did not dare. He, it seems, is highly esteemed at the present time.

We lived quietly—the morning at work in the laboratory, and the evening, for the most part, in our salon with friendly discussion and often with cards. Sinner that I am, I introduced a card game but a hopeless one, and as a lover of it, I furiously assaulted our good hostess when she made mistakes.[4] Apart

---

[4] Mechnikov had a hereditary passion for cards, but he was afraid to play even without money; he sat down near us when we played, and even as an observer he was agitated and flushed watching the troubles of our battle.

from these outbursts, I was quiet: in two years I did not lead a single student astray, did not provoke a single rebellion, did not construct a barricade. And I so delighted a trustee who went to bail for me that at Easter, 1873, he made me an active civil councillor and even came by himself to my apartment to congratulate me on this good news. Subsequently it will be apparent that he continued to testify before the high authorities to my loyalty during the following years also.

In the spring of '72 I went to Vienna, where my wife had finished her studies. I intended to go to Paris and London. But first of all she had to rest in some quiet nook, from the aftermath of her examinations in Petersburg and the daily running about in the Vienna clinics. For such a nook we chose quiet and beautiful Gmunden, where we settled in furnished rooms on the lake shore. We rested five days, not expecting any misfortune, but it came knocking at our door. In less than a week M. A. became very feverish, a rash appeared on her face, and she recalled that the day before she left Vienna she had to auscultate two children in a children's hospital—one with smallpox, the other with measles. At first she diagnosed her disease as measles, but then she began to doubt this, and we were obliged to call the native doctor. He diagnosed it as smallpox and said that the patient must be taken to the hospital at the community of the Sisters of Mercy, which was obliged to accept contagious patients. One can easily imagine with what feeing I went to the head of the community to declare what had happened. She apparently was afraid, but of course replied that the patient would be received, only not today—because it was necessary to prepare a room—but tomorrow, and that a stretcher would be sent for the patient. The remaining part of this memorable day and night were the worst hours of my life. (We had two rooms, and at night from my wife's bed through the door connecting the rooms a string was stretched to my bed and tied to my foot, in case she needed help in the night.) The heavy hours of the sleepless night passed, and towards morning I heard a gay voice from the next room, "Well, you know, I don't have smallpox; I have measles." I jumped up. The patient was sitting on the bed with a mirror in her hands and laughing. Early in the morning the same doctor, according to the promise he had made, came to us and in his turn was convinced that this was measles. The stretcher and the moving to the hospital were of course cancelled, and after the great grief happy days followed. Because of this, however, we had to spend two superfluous weeks in Gmunden. We were in Paris probably about a month. We were in all the museums, parks and gardens, in St. Cloud and Versailles, saw at the Comedie Francaise the exquisite actor, Fo (in the play "Le Gendre de M. Poirier"), heard a delightful tenor at the Opera Comique, were in the Palais Royal theater, avoided most of the streets on the national holiday (July 14), admired the gay dances of the Parisians in the open air, in a word, we lived in Paris in a most pleasant way in spite of the unbearable heat of that summer. At the end of July we went to London. Here M. A., besides sightseeing, began to go to the main hospitals. And I, because of the shortness of time (I could stay there only three weeks) and because of my inability to speak English, could not derive benefits from my stay in London, and in the middle of August I left directly for Odessa. M. A. stayed some time more in London where our close friend, Vladimir Kovalevskiy, was at this time. On the way back she spent some time in Holland (in Utrecht) with the famous ophthalmologist, Spollein, and came via Vienna to Odessa for several days in order to leave for Kiev and Professor Ivanov. At Christmas she was our guest in Odessa, and in the summer of 1873 she and I went to Tver' Province to her mother's village.

During the winter of '73 and in the beginning of '74 I was up to my ears in work. We passed the summer in Crimea.

In the winter of 1875 there came to Odessa a company of three active civil councillors, with a privy councillor at their head, making a round of all Russian universities with an original mission—to ask all Russian professors, namely, each taken separately, what we thought about the introduction of state examinations which were intended, of course, and which we had already decided beforehand by Germany's example. Why did they need to trouble dignitaries and not act in a simpler way—distribute the same question in a circular to all the universities for discussion of it in departments and councils? For the opinions of boards would have been in any case more valuable than the answers of separate persons in conversations which lasted not hours each, but minutes (the conversation with me, for example, lasted not more than two minutes). This was the first act of mistrust of the university boards and perhaps also a misgiving that they would find this measure awkward for Russia (and so it actually turned out), and their testimonial to pigeon-hole it would be less convenient than verbal answers written by the Commission itself, without any control. Perhaps even the Commission was to become acquainted in their way with the professors' way of thinking, not only on this question but also on university matters in general. When I arrived at the fixed hour in the privy councillor's apartment, the confession of my predecessor, K., (Mechnikov often well compared him with a rotten nut—nothing in appearance and good-for-nothing trash inside) was not yet finished and outbursts of gay laughter reached my ears! (I was sitting in the next room.) Hardly anything was said about the two principal questions—whether state examinations were necessary and how they should be arranged. It would be interesting to know how much this original interviewing of persons cost; contrary to expectation, each of them according to rank received an allowance of 12 horses, travelled about 3000 versts[5] and were on their journey about two months receiving, of course,

[5] 2000 miles. *Translator*

a daily allowance of about 10 rubles. But this was only a prelude to the grandiose farce which would not leave the scene of Russian life for about 20 years in the name of state examinations and would repay itself for only six universities (not counting Warsaw, Dorpat, the Medical Academy and two technological institutes) in the following way: each year the 22 chairmen of the Examination Commission are sent to the 22 departments with a recompense of 1000 rubles each; half of this probably goes as recompense for his assistant and the examiners and the lion's share for the use of the highest chairman of all the Commission (this was Mr. G., made famous by his love for his son). In such a way, this comedy cost the public coffers more than 600,000 rubles in 20 years, and meanwhile this was a comedy not in the figurative but in the true sense of the word. Teachers examined their students as before, following of course not the fiscal examination programs, but that which they themselves had given; and also on the score of lenience towards knowledge of future officials an essential change did not take place. Whoever was strict on his non-state examinations remains the same even now and vice versa.

While Mr. Delyanov's Commission was drawing us out, the minister himself, Count Dmitriy Andreyevich Tolstoy, visited Odessa, making a tour of educational institutions in southern Russia. He had come to Odessa from Feodosiya. Wishing to discuss university matters with the professors, he invited us to his apartment by departments—first the philologists, then lawyers, and, in the last turn, us, the natural scientists. There was of course a trustee present at this reception who presented each of us by name to the minister. When my turn came he said the following in a very friendly way: "In Feodosiya I had the pleasure of meeting your niece; she answered excellently for me in history." He heard out my declaration, that the department of mathematics was expelled from the biology section unjustly, so politely; but Mechnikov's words, that in Germany high school students were studying taxonomy of plants and animals, and we must teach this to the students, he heard out absent-mindedly, almost yawning. And here favorable reports were made every year concerning my conduct by the trustee, a man close to him. But this is not all. Not long before this, Mr. Tsion left the natural science department of Petersburg University, where he had been an extraordinarius professor, and the University, wishing to have me for his place without degradation to the extraordinaries, asked the ministry whether this were possible. The minister, since he was in Odessa, obviously knew about this. Before his arrival the Odessa duma, petitioning to get a polytechnic institute, gave a dinner in his honor, to which all the University professors were also invited. Taking leave of us after the dinner, the minister asked me whether I wished to be transferred to Petersburg, and receiving my consent and thanks for an answer, he transferred me in the spring of the following year. Because of my double move—from the Medical Academy to Odessa, and from Odessa to Petersburg University someone remarked, not without wit: "Sechenov spent five years on passage from Vyborg to Vasil'yev Island."

Thus having described my life in Odessa outside of the laboratory, I will pass on to a description of what I did in the laboratory.

For almost the 5 years here I studied the question of the state of CO_2 in the blood, and this question, quite simple in appearance, demanded for its solution not only experiments on all the principal component parts of the blood separately and in various combinations with each other, but to a still greater extent experiments with a long series of salt solutions.

I, of course, will not describe these experiments and will stop only on the point of the problem I undertook and the means for its realization.

The process called in physiology respiratory exchange of carbonic acid consists of: the blood, flowing through the body tissues, takes the carbonic acid created in them, and flowing through the lung, gives it to the air cavity of the latter. If one imagines for a minute that water instead of blood flowed through our veins, that with the capability of the latter of dissolving carbonic acid and giving it up by means of diffusion to the atmospheric air it could apparently take the place of blood very well. If one imagines further, blood replaced by a weak solution of sodium carbonate not fully saturated with carbonic acid to the formation of a bicarbonate, then this liquid also could apparently function successfully—to draw CO_2 in the tissues to saturation and give up the surplus drawn in the lung, since bicarbonate in the air loses CO_2. In accordance with the latter in the blood, with alkaline reaction of the liquid part, the presence of Na_2CO_3 was demonstrated, not entirely converted into bicarbonate, and in this way the activity of the blood in the matter of freeing the body from carbonic acid was reduced in essence to the presence in it of carbonic acid salt. Besides that, it was found that a certain part of CO_2 is contained in the red blood corpuscles, but it is unknown in what state. Finally, it was shown in the experiments that in the liquid part of the blood there were no substances capable of decomposing carbonic acid alkalies in a vacuum.

In this way, it is evident that the important question of the freeing of the body from CO_2 by respiration (in twenty-four hours a person breathes out about 2 pounds of CO_2) is directly connected with the question about the state of CO_2 in the blood.

The state of a gas absorbed by liquids can be studied in general in two ways: observing the various conditions of its isolation from the liquid, or, on the other hand, studying the conditions of its absorption by liquids, and the second is undoubtedly more fruitful than the first because in its direct evidences are contained also the opposite evidences—in the conditions for absorption of the gas and the conditions of its separation. Both of these methods were started by my predecessors, and they gave a great deal of valuable individual results, but on the basic question they did not proceed farther than what has been told above.

Having taking upon myself the problem of studying the state of CO_2 in the liquid part of the blood and in the red blood corpuscles, I proceeded by the second way, for which purpose I had to set up an absorptiometer under the poor conditions of the Odessa University workshops.

Whoever knows with what difficulty a new thing demanding many devices is set going will understand how much time and effort were spent on some of the preparations; and then I was faced with working with such a complex liquid as blood. From the very first steps it turned out that although Na_2CO_3 also plays an important role in the absorption of CO_2 by the liquid part of the blood, nevertheless it absorbs it in the blood differently than in a pure water solution. This circumstance compelled me to become acquainted in general with the nature of absorption of CO_2 by solutions of salts formed by weak acids. Having entered upon this field of absorptiometry not yet tested by any-one, I could not but be carried away by the comparative easiness in obtaining true results, and in this way, my work broke down into two parts—with blood and solution of salts. The business was delayed greatly through this, but there was no cause for regret because the experiments with salts gave in themselves valuable results, and in any case they helped in understanding the phenomena presented by the blood.

The experiments were begun with the liquid part of the blood (with the serum), and first of all it was necessary to make sure of its alkalinity by analyses and by direct experiments, how far the absorptiometric properties of this liquid were constant, and whether they remained a long time. Then there was the long story of the arrangement of the general nature of CO_2 absorption by this liquid, and when all this was done, I obtained a result which com-pelled me to deviate towards salt. Thanks to this deviation I found the true means of determining the magnitude of chemical absorption in the serum, and the possibility came of establishing the general nature of the chemical absorp-tion of CO_2 by the serum, as a case of chemical combination of this gas with an alkali weaker than the combination of CO_2 with Na_2CO_3 in aqueous solu-tions of the latter. The significance of this fact can be expressed thus.

The liquid part of the blood is organized in the matter of carrying out its respiratory function better than water and better than an aqueous solution of carbonic acid—it draws CO_2 into the tissues more strongly than water and gives it up in the lung cavity better than bicarbonate.

Such a find could be explained only by the fact that the alkali in the liquid part of the blood is not free, and is combined with a substance of an acid nature which limits the combinations of alkali with carbonic acid in quantity and gives this combination an observed degree of mobility. According to this, subsequent experiments were directed towards a search for such a substance in the serum, but I did not succeed in getting it separately. The only hint to the fact that this substance could be globulin was given by the experiment of adding some salt, $MgSO_4$ to the serum—the liquid remaining after the precipitation of the globulin showed only extremely weak signs of weak chemical absorption of CO_2.

The experiments with solutions of red blood corpuscles came out, beyond all expectation, much simpler, thanks to the fact that I had horse blood at hand. The fact is that from it one succeeds in obtaining, by way only of repeated freezing and settling (the liquid from a mashed blood clot) a mass of hemoglobin crystals settling from the liquid (upon standing on ice) with the appearance of thick porridge, through which came the possibility of comparing by absorptiometry the undiluted solution of corpuscles, the liquid remaining after the precipitation of the hemoglobin, and the hemoglobin itself. The result turned out so unexpected that Hoppe-Seyler was in doubt about the correctness of my experiments (I found this out from Dr. Drozdov, to whom Hoppe-Seyler expressed his doubts), being guided by the fact that according to his own experiments CO_2 does not change the spectrum of hemoglobin. Nevertheless, there was no mistake in my experiments, and there could not be, in view of the circumstance that the absorptiometric nature of the chemical absorption of CO_2 by hemoglobin appeared with the greatest clarity with a vast quantity of absorption. Along with this, the experiments showed that the combination of hemoglobin with CO_2 belongs to the class of weak combinations, i.e., depending in magnitude on pressure. At a temperature of 37° this dependence reaches the point where absorption takes place almost according to Dalton's law. With this it is important to note that the chemical bond between hemoglobin and CO_2 in general is much weaker than its bond with O_2, especially at the temperature of the animal body; consequently, the displacement of CO_2 from the hemoglobin by oxygen during breathing takes place with great ease. On the other hand, the vastness of CO_2 absorption by the thick solution of blood corpuscles as well explains to a certain extent the advantage of the arrangement of blood from an alkaline liquid and of the minutest specks floating in it, with a high content of hemoglobin. Since the main mass of O_2 inspired can unite with hemoglobin, the corpuscles have long been considered the transmitters of O_2 from the external atmosphere into the tissues, but these same corpuscles, because of their high absorption capacity for CO_2, can be considered the transmitters of CO_2 from the tissues to the external air environment of the animal. The respiratory exchange between the blood and tissues probably takes place in the following manner: the blood corpuscles, losing the

O_2 here, become by this more capable of drawing CO_2; a very great mass of this gas enters from the tissues, of course, into the liquid part of the blood; but since the combinations of it with the latter also belong to the class of weak chemical combinations, consequently, the portion of carbonic acid drawn by it cannot but be carried to the blood corpuscles—and not only the portion of gas in solution, but also the chemically bound gas. This passage must be accomplished during the flowing of the blood through the veins, and here the fine parcelling out of the blood corpuscles, as the enormous increase of their surface of contact with the liquid presents a very advantageous condition for such a passage. Such participation of the blood corpuscles in the matter of secretion of CO_2 from the body probably has the more vital significance the more CO_2 develops in the tissues, or the more it enters the body with the inspired air, because the absorption capacity for CO_2 increases in the corpuscles with an increase in pressure incomparably faster than in the liquid part of the blood.

It will be more convenient to describe my work with salts at Odessa in connection with its continuation and end at the Petersburg University laboratory.

I transferred from Odessa to Petersburg in the beginning of May, 1876, and I spent 12 years at Petersburg University.

(Almost two months—illness at first, then the war with Japan—have passed since the time when these lines were written. The misfortune is being an old man no longer useful for anything in such a grave time—you are worried by anxious expectations and your useless hands fall. I will try again to escape from the present into the past.)

8

PROFESSORSHIP IN PETERSBURG UNIVERSITY (1876-1888)

I REMEMBER the trip from Odessa to Petersburg for the fact that on the day after the trip there was that memorable May frost of a $-6°$ over all Russia, to the Caucasus and Crimea inclusive, by which the tree vegetation was delayed almost to the middle of summer. I came from the south in summer clothes, of course, stopped at my brother-in-law, Mikhaylovskiy's, and having to present myself to the minister the next day I was obliged to go there in my brother-in-law's raccoon fur coat. The university authorities received me in a friendly way and gave me leave for vacation time. I spent the summer at my wife's estate, and from this time our family life became, finally, settled without temporary separations and trips from place to place. We took up residence on Vasil'yev Island, this nice, university part of the city, since all our relatives and friends (among them also Sofiya Vasil'yevna Kovalevskaya and her husband) lived there.

At this time I am filled with great respect for Petersburg University of that time and for its physics-mathematics department in particular. Not speaking about the fact that to sit side by side with such people as Chebyshev, Mendeleyev and Butlerov was a great honor for me—the University board of that time offered a striking example of friendly unanimity on all vital questions of university life. Regularly visiting the meetings of the department and of the council during all 11 years, I was not a witness anywhere to a single hostile clash or a rude word. But meanwhile the University at that time was living through very difficult times, and sometimes it had to indulge in very delicate questions. It is known that in the '70's of the past century, the government reaction against anarchistic terror reached a climax and was expressed in part by a whole series of extremely severe administrative-police influences on the lives of the students. It went so far that students involved in university dis- orders were deprived, upon finishing their courses, of rights of entering the government service, i.e., they were deprived of their rights for disciplinary delinquencies. Mr. Delyanov's unfortunate regulations, which separated the students from the professors by a gulf, did not yet exist at that time, and the Petersburg professorial board did not consider it their right to be silent. At the suggestion of several professors a commission was formed for consideration of the matter and compilation of a memorandum in defense to the minister, and this was done. There were only two men at the council who did not sign this memorandum, Sreznevskiy and Vladislavlev (Vladislavlev was later made rector, probably for this deed). Of course, it came to nothing—the minister answered the board with a reproof and with the observation that the care of the students' fate was given to the authorities, and not to the professors.

Another cause for remembering this period of Petersburg life with love and respect was the Bestuzhev women's courses where I was a teacher for several years, and I could in fact satisfy myself of the serious significance of this sincerely noble institution. This was a women's university with two departments, in the real sense of the word, arising from private initiative and supported almost exclusively by its own means. This was at the same time an extremely original educational institution, in which the head—good, kind, honest Nadezhda Vasil'yevna Stasova—and her helpers worked without re- muneration, putting into the business not only their whole soul, but also their own pockets and maintaining discipline in the institution not by strong measures and orders but by loving regard for their pupils, persuasion, and kindness. That this was a university is shown by the systematic character of the 4-year course given by professors, docents of the university, and even several academicians. I lectured for courses in the same way and to the same extent as in the university, and giving examinations every year in both places on what I had given in lecture, I found as a result that one year the men students would do better on examinations and another year the women would. I even remember that for all my more than 40 years as a professor a woman student, and not a man, wrote the best examination for me; she was the daughter of a famous German excavator of Greek antiquities by his first marriage. Yes, this was the dawn of higher education for women in Russia, and the women students studied really with enthusiasm—I more than once saw how they studied within the walls of their university (the building of courses in the tenth line of Vasil'yev Island) after dinner. And how could it have been otherwise: few went there from boredom or from fashion, and the majority strove consciously and unselfishly for education as a higher blessing —I say "unselfishly" because at that time it did not give the women students any rights, and later it even deprived them of some. It was clear in advance for whoever knew the good, meek head of the institution that here a spirit of love and indulgence reigned; and meanwhile, life with the courses flowed more peacefully than in the institutions with strong measures and orders. In all my years of professorship for the courses there, only once was there a disturbance which drew the attention of the highest authority. The students felt—whether justly or not I do not know—that one of their friends was a spy, and they became very worried, insisting on her being sent away from classes. Rumor of this reached the above-mentioned head authority, the district trustee, and he presented himself to Nadezhda Vasil'yevna with a request for her to suppress the rebellion and defend the culprit (perhaps an innocent person) of the scandal, observing that in institutions spies were indispensable—the trustee at that time was a general and was notable for his great naïveté. Nadezhda Vasil'yevna undertook to protect the culprit of the scandal, but not because of the usefulness of that profession which was attributed to her by her fellow students, but because "My father, a general," said Nadezhda Vasil'yevna, "taught us to consider spying an indecent thing." I personally heard this from Nadezhda Vasil'yevna. There is no doubt that in those troubled times there were occasions of individual students' participation in more or less important political offenses discovered; and this circumstance, with the then groundless mistrust of students in political suspicion, affected those who heard the Bestuzhev courses in the following way. It reached the authorities that the Bestuzhev students, leaving the institution with certificates of having finished the course, did not use these certificates[1] for obtaining a position, but used the certificates from the secondary educational institutions which they had received before entering the courses (without such certificates they were not accepted for the courses). Therefore, on one fine morning the Petersburg chief of police, Gresser, demanded and obtained from the courses certificates of the secondary educational institutions of all Bestuzhev students and returned them after a short time with the supplement of stamps deliberately manufactured for them in which it appeared that the bearer was a Bestuzhev student. It is clear that along with this an order was given about banning persons with such stamps from teaching. At this time the teacher of theology courses was the rector of the Petersburg seminary, archpriest Rozanov—and even he, in a conversation with me, found this measure a little exaggerated. Not less original was the very late

---

[1] It goes without saying that the certificates did not give any rights.

rehabilitation of the Bestuzhev students in the eyes of the authority. Not long before the order to close the courses, Mr. Delyanov found this establishment harmful even in respect to morals; but as soon as these courses were left to exist in spite of him, and a crown director was placed at their head with a 3000-ruble salary and also the same inspectress with assistants (the courses themselves had to pay a salary of 8000 rubles to all these people), the institution turned out to be a decent and respectable one.

In any case, the Bestuzhev courses in the first period of their existence present an edifying example of what private initiative could do in Russia if it were given full range.

At the end of the 70's it was not especially pleasant to live in Petersburg, or in the university section of the city: the streets swarmed with "peajackets" for the observation of inhabitants outside their homes, and inside their homes the dwellers were under the supervision of the porters, and through them under the supervision of the servants. In the most troubled years of this grave time I lived with my wife on the fourth line, almost on the corner of Bolshoy Prospekt, and one time directly opposite us in the fifth line was a house which was probably very suspicious for the police. Our servant at that time, a very kind, good woman, regarded not without interest the difficulties of the service "agents" who were on duty day and night at the corner of our street and Bolshoy Prospekt, acknowledging at the same time that they received good renumeration of 50 rubles a month. At night, by her words, one of the agents got a chair from our porter and taking up quarters in the garret of our house, kept his eye on the upper stories of the opposite one. Fortunately our servant did not have treacherous inclination of listening behind the doors, and we personally lived through this time of troubles all right. However, I nevertheless had occasion accidentally to come in touch with a story which originated with the information of a servant. During these same years one of my pupils, V., the most capable of all those who worked in my laboratory, lived with his two sisters as a family, i.e., they rented a common apartment, kept a cook, and cooked at home. The brother was finishing the course in the university, the older sister was studying medical courses, and the younger sister was a Bestuzhev student, compiled lectures in physics and lithographed them, after which there was a great deal of used paper and proof sheets in the apartment. This circumstance seemed suspicious to the cook, and through her denunciation one fine night they took all three, after a thorough search of the furniture, mattresses of the beds, and even the walls (I found this out from the arrested ones). I learned of the fate which overtook them from one of V.'s friends the next day after the arrest, and also found out from the same person that the arrest was made not by the secret, but the manifest, police.

Knowing V. in the course of several years as a man who studied scientific problems with a passion and with success—he studied nerves and not politics (at this time he had already printed an excellent work in the German *Pflüger's Archiv*), and being sure, therefore, of his political innocence, I wrote an extensive memorandum and presented myself with it at the usual receiving hours to the police chief, Gresser. At first he began to make excuses when I declared that V. was arrested by his police, but finally he took pity, made inquiries, and making sure of the justice of my declaration, he asked me to come to him for an answer after about two days, which I, of course, did. Upon my appearance in his office, he ordered the arrested ones brought and he set them free with the admonition to be careful in such times (not considering, of course, such a necessity for his agents), and when they had gone out he let me go with the declaration that it was impossible to trust present-day youth.

At that time in Petersburg lived a big company of relatives: my older sister Anna Mikhaylovna (a favorite of my wife) and her husband, N. A. Mikhaylovskiy; my brother Rafail and his wife, Yekaterina Vasil'yevna (née Lyapunova) and their daughter, Natasha, two Lyapunov brothers, students (Yekaterina Vasil'yevna's nephews), whom I knew still as children; and the Krylov family: the husband (Nikolay Aleksandrovich), his wife, Sofiya Viktorovna, their son, Aleksey (a future sailor), a sister-in-law, Aleksandra Viktorovna, and a little French ward, Victor Henri. All these were simple, first-rate people. The older ones were peacefully living the rest of their days, and the youth studied with such zeal and success that all four became well-known scientists. At the present time Aleksandr Mikhaylovich Lyapunov is a distinguished mathematician and academician; his brother, Boris Mikhaylovich is a professor at Odessa and a very learned Slavicist; Aleksey Krylov is a mathematician-inventor and shipbuilder; Victor Henri is a well-known physiologist-psychologist. Of my university colleagues I became friends most of all with good, kind Dmitriy Konstantinovich Bobylevskiy, kept up an acquaintance with the family of Andrey Nikolaye-vich Beketov, and visited Dmitriy Ivanovich Mendeleyev, Fedor Fomich Petrushevskiy and Professor Posse. Besides this, I became acquainted with the families of Al. Nik. Pypin and Nadezhda Vasil'yevna Stasova.

It is clear that my non-university life was spent primarily at home in the circle of my own people at harmless idleness in the form of hopeless vint, readings of literary news and even choral singing, since old Krylov knew many gay Russian songs and my brother Rafail was a great lover of singing.

As recently as just last year (1903), Nikolay Aleksandrovich Krylov on a trip through Moscow enticed me to go to Petersburg for a singing soirée.

Recollecting this life in my circle of relatives I cannot but recall the following circumstance. In my youth in the engineering college I studied mathematics zealously, but when I left there I entirely abandoned it—at first because of medicine, the study of which lasted 9.5 years (6 years in university and 3.5 abroad), then because of the daily physiology work which did not demand anything except a most elementary mathematical knowledge. Nevertheless, from time to time I regretted that everything which had been acquired in former times in youth had begun to decay so easily long, long ago. The year when Al. Mikh. Lyapunov was finishing the course in the mathematics department of Petersburg University, I was enticed, finally, by the possibility of recalling with his help what I had long forgotten, and I started taking lessons from him, along with this studying independently in the textbooks of Schlömilch. I got through Schlömilch's textbook on higher analysis in a year, but I did not go further—physiological work again engulfed me, but perhaps also because I was already old for setting out on new lines.

I will cite two more of the other events of this period of Petersburg life: an event with the Academy of Sciences and an event with the title of an honored professor.

I have already told above that thanks to the recommendation of the Odessa trustee Golubtsov, Dmitriy Andreyevich Tolstoy, who was very friendly to me, transferred me to Petersburg. Here during the first years his good favor evidently continued because once I, along with Professor Orest Müller, was honored by being invited to his house for dinner, where we both, however, had the appearance not of dear guests, but of one possessed, since the hostess of the house,[2] nodding her head to us from afar throughout the whole dinner, did not honor us with a look or a word. Probably Dmitriy Andreyevich's favorable disposition towards me continued even further when he became Minister of Internal Affairs and President of the Academy of Sciences, because unexpectedly and unforetold for me Yagich (then a professor in the university and an academician) turned to me with the question of would I come to the Academy if they were to choose me. At this time there was nothing for me to fear of "red ears," and I gave my consent. After this, Ovsyannikov asked me for a list of my works; the business of presentation proceeded, and it became known to me that I was chosen for the department. Soon after that, to my good fortune,[3] the following circumstance occurred. The affair was in the spring on the morning of the holiday of Ascension; I was going along Vasil'yev Island quay to the laboratory, and not far from the University, probably lost in thought, I passed a man coming to meet me, not recognizing his face. But having gone past, I know that this was Dmitriy

---

[2] The daughter of the famous Kiev satrap Bibikov.
[3] I will indicate later why I have said "to my good fortune," and not "unfortunately" here.

Andreyevich. Had I recognized him at the moment when I met him I would not have failed to greet him, but now it was too late to turn back with an apology, and I did not return. After several days they reported to me that the president of the academy had placed a veto on my election, and I was not admitted to the balloting in the general meeting.

It is possible that my other fiasco also was somewhat connected with this academy incident, although the figure here was another count—Ivan Davydovich. I do not remember how, whether I myself guessed or who advised me, but in 1887 I recalled that I had been a professor 27 years, and minus the year leave between the Medical Academy and Odessa University— more than 26. When I announced this in the university office, the matter was raised about my presentation for a title of honored professor. Time passed then, but, once I was seated in the council, and among other things, a paper from the minister was read in which there was a refusal for my presentation be- cause, they say, from the 26 years the 10 years must be deducted which I spent as a professor in the Medical Academy. I must remark that on me first fell the letter of the law according to which the title of honor could be received only by persons who had been a professor 25 years in the Univer- sity, because just a year before, years of professorship at Gorygorets Institute were accepted for a professor of statistics as university service. This was especially inconsistent since the Medical Academy, as a medical department, was entirely equivalent to the university departments. On these grounds, on the reading of the minister's note, the president (Andrey Nikolayevich Beketov) turned to the council with the question did it not find it necessary to turn to the minister with the request that the decision heard be changed. But before the council could express itself, I, for my part turned to him with a request not to do this since a concession on the part of the minister would have the meaning of mercy shown to me, and I could accept mercy only from the sovereign, but not at all from the minister. Many years later, in Moscow, to my great chagrin, and of course without knowledge on my part, they nevertheless promoted me to honors, and I in such a way was deprived of the original title which I wished, "unhonored professor," in spite of 40 years of professorship.

Of non-university events from the time of my stay in Petersburg I should note Gruber's last jubilee, S. P. Botkin's 25 year jubilee, and the banquet in honor of General Radetskiy, at the end of the last Turkish war.

With us in Russia, Gruber fully deserved the jubilee with his diligence rare in our country, and his exemplary implementation of the responsibilities which he took upon himself. Having, moreover, the naïveté to measure his services by the number of anomalies he found every day, he considered jubilees a tribute of honor to his eruditeness, and passionately loved these festive occasions with their laudatory speeches and gifts. Knowing this weakness of his, Gruber's friends and admirers arranged three jubilees for him for 45 years of his professorship in Russia, and he described all three, with all the documents in German, and published it in Vienna. Gruber's jubilees started with the greetings of his subordinates in the anatomy theater; after these followed the reception of the deputation in one of the halls of the Medical Academy; from here the festivities were moved for friends to his apartment and concluded with a jubilee dinner at which he solemnly appeared, with his faithful Husti on his arm, who went along happily with a bouquet in her arms, with a radiant face and tears in her eyes. The happiness of the honest toiler, Gruber, and his good, faithful wife was really touching.

Botkin's jubilee bore another character and was, in my opinion, spoiled by a superfluous splendor and by the fact that the festive occasion was given the character of a celebration in honor of the hero of the day not so much by the scholars as by the city and its municipal representative as master, as if Botkin's title as a member of the duma went before his scholarly merits. The festive occasion in the hall of the City Duma began with a musical cantata composed for this occasion by Balakirev; as soon as the hero of the day showed up in the hall he was met by a thunder of applause. For him and all those close to him a platform was arranged so high over those present that the speakers had to raise their heads a great deal to the face of Botkin, who was standing on the platform. At the conclusion of everything, the town mayor recalled the name of Newton in a speech. Such overdoing it, although it was usual in Russian jubilees, was very displeasing to me; some of the people in attendance noticed this and it seems they concluded envy on my part, but there was really nothing to envy: the position of one on his name day has always seemed to me a little silly, and I have avoided name days and celebrations of honor all my life; and even Botkin himself declared to me after all his festivities that to endure jubilee celebrations was an unpleasant duty.

The Petersburg generals honored General Radetskiy, as a former pupil of the engineering college, with a festive dinner at the end of the last Turkish war. General Aleksandr Ivanovich Savel'yev, a former officer on duty in my guide group, invited me to this dinner as a guest. At the head table opposite General Radetskiy sat: the chairman of the banquet, General Kaufman and the two principal guests, Dostoyevskiy and Grigorovich (both had been pupils at the college); at a separate table opposite the middle of the table of honor sat Aleksandr Ivanovich Savel'yev, my comrade in the college (a year younger than I), General Leyer, a known strategist and later the head of the general staff academy, Ewald, a former teacher of physics in my guide class, and myself. Leyer gave the first speech of a military content: after him Grigorovich (Dostoyevskiy was silent for some reason) very gaily and glibly described the old orders in the college; after this, Ewald said a few very clever words, and then they demanded that I also speak. If I had known that this would happen I would have been prepared, but now I had to extemporize. Fortunately, I still remembered the principal episodes of the war with which the name of Radetskiy was connected and his first crossing of the Danube, the defense of Shipka Pass and the later battle beyond the Balkans which ended the war. I recalled all this, but in such an unimportant form that the speech was not successful. In print it came out very beautifully thanks to the fact that a day or two after the banquet Radetskiy's adjunct came to me, it seems, and brought my speech to show it to me, as if he had written it down, but it was essentially a list he himself had compiled very well of those facts which I had recalled awkwardly. How Radetskiy responded to toasts I do not remember, but I know that he offered a toast to the Russian soldier. After the people began to get up from the table Dostoyevskiy whispered to me that I call for a toast to the fathers and mothers of the Russian soldier, i.e., to the Russian people, and with this toast the dinner ended. After dinner, meeting several of my former teachers, now grayed generals (among them was Pauker—lieutenant while I was a guide, and now it was almost the day before his appointment as Minister of Means of Communication), and several of my comrades, was for me a great joy. From these meetings youth was involuntarily savored, and they have remained a very sweet memory in my soul. Of my comrades, by the way, I met General Zeyme, who was degraded in former times from sergeant-major to private. He with a smile recalled our past failures.

I will pass now to my life in the Petersburg laboratory.

The conditions were more than modest. The laboratory consisted in all of two rooms—one for the professor, the other for his assistant; the allowance of instruments was very little, the budget was little, and in addition to all this, the first two to three years until I had trained two efficient assistants from the new students, I had to remain without a proper assistant. Nevertheless, I worked very successfully here and qualitatively did more in essence than in any of my former laboratories. One of the works which my former investigations had concluded was the absorption of CO_2 by saline solutions, and another, experiments with inhibiting influences in the sphere of the nervous system. Moreover, side by side with the successes, which brought many good moments in life, there were also many griefs, brought in two cases by my own blunders and in one by a temporary inability to carry through the work of many years. All this will be described in its place.

Upon first acquiring my new place, so as not to sit without work, I went to Petersburg with a ready plan to continue the Odessa experiments with saline solutions. With this object, immediately upon my arrival in Petersburg (in the beginning of May), I ordered from a well-known, excellent mechanic[4] (I have forgotten his name) an absorptiometer so that it should be ready for September, and that it would meet a series of conditions stipulated beforehand. He refused to estimate even the approximate value of the instrument when it was ordered, pleading the impossibility of indicating beforehand how much of his time the apparatus would take since he had never made such instruments; but the mechanic was known as an extremely conscientious man, and I left for a summer in the country without any misgivings. In September the instrument was ready and met all the conditions stipulated excellently, but then its cost was announced to me—500 rubles instead of the 150-200 I had expected—I was stupefied, because the fee was equivalent to two month's salary, and I lived almost exclusively on my salary. Nevertheless, the mechanic was right because he was brought up on work with astronomical instruments which demanded almost mathematical precision, was used to working with the greatest thoroughness, and justly valued such work very highly. The fee, not entirely within my means, was of course quickly forgotten, and then I had only to be glad for the instrument which afforded me the possibility of noticing with certainty finer things than the instrument with which I worked at Odessa.

Above, in the description of my work at Odessa with blood, I already casually mentioned why I digressed from blood to saline solutions, and now I will describe my whole train of thought which called forth this digression, which lasted for years.

As soon as I had established for the serum, by experiments, a significant dependence of the chemical absorption upon pressure, I thought that for an explanation of the fact it would be sufficient to perform in greater detail the experiments of my predecessors in this field (Ferne and L. Meyer with Heidenhain) with solutions of Na_2CO_3 and Na_2HPO_4, and this was done; but the results I received did not explain the fact, and this circumstance compelled me to seek a possible answer in the absorption of CO_2 by solutions of other salts capable of binding CO_2 chemically. It is very possible the digression this way would have come to an end very quickly if I had not come upon solutions of acetous soda in my own research. The results I obtained with this salt were so unexpected and interesting that to stop these experiments would have been impossible, the more so as the field into which

---

[4] He was the old mechanic at the Pulkov Observatory; he did not get along with the director of the above and had the misfortune to be transferred to Petersburg to establish a workshop here. In spite of the fact that this was a master of the first-hand, his affairs went badly and he ended tragically.

fate threw me was not yet touched by anyone. It was impossible not to go forward, and experiments with three new salts were added to the material already collected. When, after this, all the experiments with seven different salts were compiled with each other, with the acids in the order of increasing strength, then it turned out that in my hands there was already sufficient material for establishing the general nature of the *weak chemical absorption* of CO_2 by salt solutions.

At the head of the series were two salts of almost equal strengths of acidity, CO_2 and NaH_2PO_4, and their solutions were notable in that with a sufficient degree of dilution the salt reacted with CO_2 as a whole, and namely, that CO_2 took from the salt solution half of its base, then as in dense solutions, the quantity of chemical absorption lagged behind this limit the thicker the solution was. After these salts came those in which the chemical reaction did not reach the above-mentioned limit, not under any degree of dilution, although here too as in the preceding cases, the relative quantity of chemical absorption is increased by the extent of dilution of the solutions. To the third group belonged the salts which constituted the transition from the preceding to the salts formed by strong mineral acids. In one of these there were still clear signs of an insignificant chemical absorption of CO_2, i.e., signs that CO_2 took from the salt solution an insignificant part of its base, but in solutions of another salt these signs almost disappeared, and the absorption already took place according to Dalton's Law—the solution of gases in liquids. How could one not draw the following two conclusions:

1) The nature of a chemical reaction with salt solutions is everywhere one and the same—everywhere CO_2 takes from the salt solution part of its base and, other things being equal, the less—the stronger the acid of the salt, and the more—the more dilute its solution, and,

2) The strength of the mineral acids is not infinitely great in comparison with the strength of CO_2; consequently, also for the salt solutions formed by mineral acids, degrees of dilution must exist under which the chemical reaction becomes clear.

It was very difficult to withstand the temptation of the second conclusion, and I was drawn to experiments on this question, which ended in failure (success followed many years later in Petersburg).

I, of course, could have come to a stop here because salts with strong acids did not promise anything for the chemical absorption of CO_2 by blood; but if one takes into account that the absorptiometric experiment had entirely not touched this region yet and had promised much new, then it becomes clear that I could not stop. The experiments with blood went in their own sequence, and along with them went the working out of the problem of whether it was impossible to bring salt solutions indifferent to CO_2 into a definite system, just as this was successful for salts the solutions of which absorb CO_2 chemically.

According to this, it was first of all necessary to solve the problem: how can one measure the salt solutions well enough for a comparison of them with each other from the aspect of their absorbing capacity. In this I was influenced by the following considerations: if for such quantities a general true criterion exists, then one can find it only under the following condition: if equal or equivalent quantities of salts—and, of course, most of all, of a similar kind,—dissolved *in the same way* in water, yield solutions of equal absorbing capacity. Fortunately, searching for such a criterion did not last long:[5] *it is necessary to take for comparison not equal, but equivalent quantities of salts in equal volumes of solutions.* Under this condition closely related salts in weak solutions and solutions of medium strength give the same coefficients of absorption of CO_2.

But just why can such a dosing serve as a general criterion for the comparison of solutions? For the following two reasons. One can consider the salt solution as the lower step of the combination of salt with water, following the combination of salt with crystallized water; the circumstance that only solutions with equivalent quantities of salts are compared is an echo of this relationship. The meaning of the second point is also clear: Dalton's law, to which the absorption of CO_2 by all liquids in general which are indifferent to this gas conforms, and such are our salt solutions, attributes the quantity of absorption to the volumes of the liquids. Along with this, the solution to equal volumes marks an equal degree of drawing apart of the salt particle—the equality of mechanical conditions of the dissociation of salt by water.

Comparison of the solutions prepared in this way showed: weak and medium strength solutions of related salts absorb equal quantities of CO_2; on the same basis: sulfates[6] possess the least absorbing capacity, after them follows the chlorides, and the nitrates absorb most of all; with the same acids: the sodium salts absorb least of all, after them go the potassium salts, and the ammonia salts absorb most of all.

To such an order of salts with different absorption capacities corresponds the different degree of their dissociation by water, or in the opposite sense, the different degree of affinity of salts for water; therefore, *the general classifying principle for the reduction of salts* (in the relation of their solutions to CO_2) *to a system can be only their relation to water.*

---

[5] Thanks to the fact that for the first test I took weak solutions of two salts so like each other as $MgSO_4$ and $ZnSO_4$.

[6] For a comparison with salts based on the same acids, two half shares of sulfate were of course taken.

These same results, in connection with the possibility shown above of looking on salt solutions as on very weak combinations of salt with water, gave grounds for thinking that CO_2 is absorbed entirely by the water of a salt solution, but the salt only limits the quantity of absorption of the gas drawing the water to itself.

My Odessa work with salts broke off on this, and it was continued in Petersburg.

Water alone was used as a solvent of salt in all the experiments described thus far, and its role in the phenomena was reduced essentially only to expanding the salt in solution to a greater volume, bringing it to a state of greater or lesser degree of dissociation. The question of whether quality of the solvent also plays a role in the phenomena remains unaffected— experiments with salt solutions in other solvents besides water were lacking. Such experiments, apart from direct interest, were necessary as a natural continuation and an end of the previous ones, where the question of the participation of the salt's composition in the phenomena was ascertained. Thus, I was faced with comparing by absorptiometry the solutions of one and the same salt, of course, taken in one and the same quantity in various solvents (for example, in water, alchohol, glycerine, etc.). By this, founded on the evidence of the preceding experiments, that the solutions compared had to be of the same volume, I should have directly dissolved like quantities of salt in various solvents to equal resulting volumes, but I thought that the results would turn out more simply if the salt would act on equal volumes of solvent. Fortunately, this blunder did not have bad consequences and was quickly corrected, and the solution of another solvent for comparison with water was, on the contrary, extremely felicitous. At first I wanted to take alcohol, since the coefficients of the CO_2 solution in it were given in Bunsen's experiments; but for experiments with alcohol I had to alter a great deal in the absorptiometer, and I decided instead of alchohol to take an aqueous solution of salt. Thus, the first experiment consisted of the comparison of the following two solutions:

NaCl + (water) and NaCl + (an $NaNO_3$ solution in water), in which equal volumes of liquids, the names of which are enclosed in parentheses, were used as solvents of one and the same quantity of NaCl.

The success of the choice as solvent of an aqueous $NaNO_3$ solution showed up immediately after it turned out from the comparison of reduced solutions that the salt added to the various solutions decreases the absorbing capacity of the latter to the same extent—which was, in other words, the following simple relation between the coefficients of solutions a and b and the coefficients of solvents σ and β.

$$a : b = \sigma : \beta$$

Just after this came the possibility of verifying whether the same relation

would not turn out between the coefficient of the following two solutions:
NaCl + (water) and NaCl + (a solution of NaCl in water), of which
in the second the NaCl solution standing on the left serves as the solvent
(in parentheses) and where, therefore, twice as much NaCl is contained in
the liquid when the volumes are equal. The expectation came true for these
solutions also: if the coefficient of the left is designated by a, the right by c,
and the coefficient of water by α, then the coefficient of the solvent in the
right solution will be a, and we receive:

$$a : c = \alpha : a,$$
$$\text{from which } c = a^2$$
$$\overline{\alpha}$$
$$\text{or when } \alpha = 1, c = a^2.$$

Subsequent experiments have been directed at the verification of this
simple relation between the coefficients of NaCl solutions when, with equality
of volumes, the content of salt in them increases from 1 to 3, 4, 5, and the
results corresponded to the expectation.

Thus, I received a twofold result: on one hand it was proved that *one
and the same quantity of salt, when it is dissolved to equal volumes in
various solvents, gives solutions the coefficients of which relate to each other
as the coefficients of the solvents do;* on the other hand, there is *a definite
numerical law of change of coefficients of a solution with the change of its
concentration or dilution by volume.*

In the first of these results there was a clear indication of the role of the
solvent in our phenomena: *the absorption capacity of any given saline solution
is in direct dependence on the absorption capacity of the solvent, and the salt in
the solution has the significance only of a factor limiting the quantity of
absorption of gas, according to the degree of its affinity for water.*

After the law was established for several solutions, it was necessary to
verify it in many other examples; with this, in the curves of absorption,
came to light manifest signs of chemical reaction of CO_2 with the salts
dissociated by water—signs more clear the more watery the solution. In
other words, here in the experiment the thought was confirmed which had
arisen in the very beginning of my work with salt solutions—that even the
salts of mineral acids in solutions had to react chemically with CO_2 since
their strength is not extremely great compared with the strength of CO_2.

*Thus, absorptiometry bound together all salts in general from clearly
decomposed ones in solutions of carbonic acid to where they were considered
indifferent to this gas, proving that the reaction of CO_2 with their solutions
is everywhere the same and everywhere consists of a dual competition of
CO_2 and salt because of the base of the latter and because of the water,*

Such a result is achieved by absorptiometry thanks to the fact that it gives with fidelity almost thousandth parts of milligrams.

The work with salts and CO_2 lasted at Petersburg, with two big interruptions, for about ten years and brought to me, along with many happy minutes, a great deal of grief. Some biologists reproached me because I, a physiologist, give up too much time and energy to the solution of non-physiological problems; and I, of course, realized the grounds for these reproofs, but I did not have the strength to tear myself away from the tempting possibility gradually turning out of finding the key to a vast class of phenomena as yet unknown to anyone. Twice I interrupted experiments with CO_2 by working on other problems, but then again I returned to them. Thanks to this, in one circle there even took shape such a stereotyped phrase as, "All that I. M. Sechenov is doing is pumping CO_2."[7] Besides, the attitude of chemists towards my work, justified to a certain extent, pained me even more. They recognized the results I obtained and considered them worthy of attention, but they considered that I should corroborate them by experiments with other gases besides the eternal CO_2. It was easy to say this, but how was I to carry out such suggestions. CO_2 was chosen for the experiments because it is absorbed by salt solutions in comparatively large quantities, and all the other convenient gases—O_2, H, N—are dissolved very weakly, so there was nothing to consider about them.

Thus, the work of many years lost its principal significance as a key to a vast class of phenomena.

I remained with this splinter in my heart to the end of my stay in Petersburg; I tried to seek consolation abroad, in Leipzig and Paris, but I found only a little comfort with my good teacher Ludwig. I reported to him all my former results with the salts of weak acids and the new results with the salts of strong acids; he looked at them from the aspect of their absorptiometric completeness, understood that it had been possible to achieve such results only by long, tenacious labor, and apparently he was left pleased with what had been done. I came to Ostwald with a manuscript résumé of the work; in the presence of several young chemists I gave him an explanation regarding this résumé; he did not make any objections, accepted the manuscript for publication (it appeared in his journal under the title "Ueb. Konstit. d. Salzlös. auf Grund ihres Verh. zu Kohlens"), but when I declared that I would like to turn over further work on these problems to more competent chemists, no one expressed interest in Ostwald's appeal to those present. I went to Paris with the idea of publishing the Petersburg part of the work in French, and I succeeded in this, with the help of Ducleau;

[7] The word "pump" comes from the fact that during the experiments I had to pump the gases out of the liquid, and then pump the receptacle with the liquid in air.

but when I was leaving I found out from a letter of Mechnikov that they considered my work important but also consider that it was poorly written up. Later, when I was in Moscow, I succeeded in strengthening by further work the significance of which I had sought, but about this, later.

In 1879 I either became tired, or "pumping carbonic acid" bored me, but only the work with it was abandoned, and I was occupied with thoughts of how the balloonists of the "Zenith" could suffocate at the height of $\frac{1}{3}$ atmosphere, i.e., I was engaged in a calculation of in what measure the income of O_2 was insufficient for breathing during each respiratory period, on the basis of the physiological data available on this subject. I correctly took 30 g. as the standard of the hourly consumption of O_2, but in changing the quantity of the respiration into cubic centimeters in one minute I made an arithmetical error—I took 700 cm^3 instead of 350, and 50 cm^3 for the respiratory period instead of 25. It is clear that on the basis of such a calculation the conclusion was erroneous—the balloonists had to suffocate at a height of $\frac{1}{2}$ atmosphere. Of course, I was very grieved when I received a letter from abroad from Zuntz in which the mistake and the erroneousness of the conclusion were pointed out; but this grief was quickly replaced by joy. The following year I made amends for the mistake with a compensating article, "Ueb. d. O—Spannung in der Lungenluft unt. versch. Beding.," printed in *Pflüger's Archiv* (v. XXII). Here with a calculation of the normal consumption of O_2 three circumstances were taken into account: the fact that blood draws O_2 from the air of the lung sacs, that losses of oxygen are made up not by the oxygen, but by atmospheric air, and that from the volume of air breathed only a more or less significant part gets into the lung sacs.

If we accept with this that respiration in all respects is accomplished with mechanical regularity, then it turns out that whatever the initial content of O_2 in the lung air, its quantity as a value depending on the value of periodic consumption of O_2 and the periodic entrance into the sacs of a certain volume of air, becomes (in the intervals between expirations and the following inspirations) more or less quickly stationary. It is clear that respiration at different depths, with invariability of the consumption of O_2 by the body and with a constant diminution of the quantity of air flowing into the lung (since the volume of inspiration remains constant but the inspired air rarefied), brings a constant diminution of the stationary quantity of O_2 in the lung, and as soon as the latter is reduced so that the partial pressure goes downwards from 20 mm. the conditions for suffocation set in.

After I had made up for my blunder in this way, it was natural to extend the reasoning which served this to other component parts of pulmonary air and expand the frame of conditions capable of influencing the stationary state of each of the three component gases of pulmonary air. Thus, in *Pflüger's Archiv* the following year (Bd. XXIV, 1881) appeared an article under the title of "Die Theorie der Lungenluftzusammensetzung." Here the following conditions influencing the stationary volumes of pulmonary gases were investigated: the capacity of the lung and the volume of inspiration; the pressure and the discharge of air from 10 atm. to 0.4 atm.; the composition of the inspired air from the aspect of CO_2 and O_2 in percentages of one and the other gas, including the case of breathing pure oxygen; variation in the consumption of O_2 and the manufacturing of CO_2 including the case of such variation in the presence of muscular work (when the volume of CO_2 produced exceeds the volume of oxygen consumed).

The other, yet longer, interruption of my "pumping CO_2" was spent on work with electrical phenomena on the spine and medulla oblongata of the frog. This work, "Galvan. Ersch. and verläng. Marke d. Frosch." appeared in *Pflüger's Archiv* in 1882 (Bd. XXVII). Here, all three forms of electromotor phenomena for the nerve already known, resting currents, electron, and negative fluctuations were first ascertained for the spinal axis of the frog, singled out from the body. Besides this—and these were the main points of the investigation—I found: a) galvanic effects of motor impulses arising spontaneously in the medulla oblongata in the form of spontaneous negative fluctuations of the current; b) inhibition of these fluctuations of respiratory impulses by strong tetanization of the sciatic nerves in a centripetal direction; c) inhibition under the same condition of excitability of the spinal cord to direct stimulation, and finally, d) intensification of the fluctuations, of respiratory impulses, after the cessation of tetanization.

The significance of all these facts arises from the following.

a) The development in the medulla oblongata of spontaneous fluctuations of current is fully analogous to the long-known development of so-called forced movements in frogs with the brain cut along the upper edge of the medulla oblongata. Whatever the primary reason for the latter, at the basis of them, in any case, lie the stimulations of the centers. This means that fact *a* first establishes some analogy between the process of stimulation of the center and the nerve, or, at least, an analogy between the external expressions of these processes.

b) Inhibition of spontaneous fluctuations by strong tetanization of sensory nerves evidently owes its occurrence to the depression of excitability of the whole spinal axis (this arises from fact *c*), fully analogous to that which is given in my experiments by the same tetanization on frogs (with hemispheres removed and on ones with the brain destroyed) in relation to reflexes, expressed in appearance by the inhibition of cutaneous sensitivity (see above).

c) Although depression of excitability of nerve centers with strong tetanization of the sensory nerves was ascertained only for the spine owing to the impossibility of application of direct stimulation to the medulla oblongata, it is still impossible to doubt that also here the effect of nerve tetanization is evidently the same—the fact of inhibition by stimulating shocks supports this.

d) The fact of the increase of spontaneous fluctuations, of respiratory stimulating shocks, following the cessation of tetanization is important in three respects, proving: 1) that inhibition of these fluctuations cannot be attributed to exhaustion or fatigue of the nerve centers; 2) that the latter during tetanization must, on the contrary, be charged with energy (otherwise the development of strong movements upon its cessation would be incomprehensible), and 3) presenting a complete analogy with the intensification of reflexes (in the frog) which I found, after the cessation of the tetanization of the nerves inhibiting them.

From facts *b* and *d* it follows, finally, obviously, that in the depression of stimulating shocks in the medulla oblongata by tetanization of the nerves brought there we have a doubtless analogy with the inhibition of heart activity by stimulation of the vagi, for, both here and there the effect takes shape not by exhaustion or fatigue of the nerve centers, presenting a case of the so-called inhibition of the activity of the organ. This analogy is supplied by Heidenhain, who repeated on the vagus nerve and the heart my experiment with stimulation of the sciatic nerve of the frog by salt and with the then posterior segment of the stimulated part: parallel to the effects I obtained, the inhibition of reflexes and their intensification, he obtained a stopping of the heart and an intensification of cardiac activity. This analogy, finally, gives us the right to conclude that in the act of diastolic stopping of the heart, inhibition of excitability of the neuro-motor mechanisms plays a definite role.

The experiments with intensification of nerve stimulation without intensification of the stimulating current by application to the nerve of three electrodes belong to this same interval of time. By Pflüger's experiments with change of stimulation on the poles of the polarizing current, with the addition to it of one of the observations of a Petersburg University student, now a professor of physiology at Odessa, Verigo, the nerve is stimulated by a stimulating current in the sphere of the catelectrotonus strongest of all under the condition that the stimulating current is applied to the nerve in such a way that its negative pole is turned to the negative pole of the polarizing current. If we therefore take three electrodes instead of two, with a branch of one of them as shown by the thick lines in the figure (fig. 2), then the application of the stimulating current (weak constant or induction shock) to the nerve in an ascending direction will correspond to the above-men-

tioned condition of the strongest stimulation of the
nerve. Experiments confirmed this supposition.

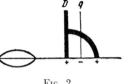

FIG. 2

I still recall a small note concerning the renal
blood formation printed at about the same time.

Among the purifiers of the blood from the no
longer used products of breaking up of substances,
the lungs and the kidneys stand first and foremost:
the first clear the blood of gas-generated substances, and the second mainly
of the products of albumin disintegration dissolved in water. The lungs, by
their volume and by their location are arranged very conveniently for the
carrying out of their work: with their very large volume they lie in the
pathway of all the blood flowing through the body, but the kidneys (clearing *all* the blood) lie to one side of its main path, to one side of the abdom-
inal aorta, and are so small that judging by their volume, only a very
insignificant quantity of blood can flow through them. The comparatively
more advantageous conditions in the arrangement of the lungs are explained
by the fact that 900 g in round numbers of a harmful substance (CO_2) are
removed by them in a day, but by the kidneys no more than 40 g, if we
do not count the harmless water. But this nevertheless does not settle the
question of how the kidneys as the cleansers *for all the blood* cope with their
task with their small volume and with their disadvantageous location to the
side of the blood's main pathway. They handle it very expeditiously as far as
one can judge by the speed with which they remove the surplus of water
from the body.[8]

It is easy to understand that such an evident disparity between the position
of the kidney in the circulatory path and its blood-purifying function could
be eliminated either by the passage through the kidney of comparatively
(with its volume) large quantities of blood or by such structure of the
organ by which conditions for intensified filtration of water were created
in the kidney. It is known that Ludwig, who drew up the filtration theory
of urination, brought in three facts which apparently spoke strongly for

[8] Direct experiments showed that the small kidneys of a rabbit in the course of several
hours were capable of removing more than 1 l. of water artificially introduced in the form
of a physiologic solution of common salt. In the student tavern at Leipzig where I dined
in former times, during my experiments on myself with the influence of alcohol on the
secretion of urea, the host usually wrote with chalk on a blackboard the names of the
evening visitors and the number of mugs of beer drunk by each of them. Once I saw,
not without wonder, the name "Motz" on this blackboard, and by it the number 34.
To my inquiries the host reported that the preceding evening Mr. Motz drank from 6
o'clock in the evening until 12 at night, 34 mugs of beer, without the least harm to himself. I saw a similar case in my family's village on the patron saint's day. Their coach-
man Semen drank almost a bucket of homebrewed beer in a short time, became swollen,
and from fear came to me, swollen, as to a doctor. Finding out what was the matter, I
calmed him, and in the evening the edema passed.

filtration: the high pressure of the blood entering the kidneys, the free position of the almost bare vessels of the malpighian body (where the water is exuded) in the urinary capsules and the quick passage of the bodies' artery to the capillary network. It is further known that the filtration theory fell; Heidenhain's experiments proved that the factor which determines the quantity of water taken out of the blood is not the pressure of the blood, but the comparative rapidity of the blood flow through the organ. On behalf of this thought, he correctly cited the especially wide opening of the renal artery in comparison with the size of the organ, but he left without proper attention the most important feature in the providing of the kidney with blood. On account of this, my note appeared. It showed that the rapidity of flow through the kidney of comparatively large quantities of blood is determined, apart from the shortness of the renal path, most of all by the huge difference of blood pressure upon entering the kidney and upon leaving it, by which a steep drop of pressures along the renal vessels takes shape at the same time.

Simultaneously with this note I published another, concerning the equalization of the force of revolving induction currents, where I, by some incomprehensible mental lapse, made a mistake in the currents in the branching conductors which a high school boy would hardly have made if he had had an elementary course in physics. This mistake tormented me considerably. Yet it was good that it happened much after Dmitriy Andreyevich rejected me for the Academy of Sciences, or else it would have been a scandal capable of worrying me to death. And I said above, in the description of my academic fiasco, that I *fortunately* did not find myself in the Academy namely for this reason.

Thus, my life at the laboratory of Petersburg University brought me many happy moments and great grief. The proofs which I already had in my hands that my work had given me a name in the West could serve as some consolation, but could it eradicate the splinter from my heart when at the end of almost ten-years' work with CO_2 I was told: "Everything that you have done is very good, but it is a particular case; prove your law with other gases in general."

Because of the positive impossibility of carrying out what was proposed, my stay at the Petersburg laboratory became pointless for me, and even unpleasant, and I decided to exchange my professorship for a more modest position as a Privatdocent in Moscow, where, according to information I had, physiology was not doing so well. With this aim, in 1888 I retired and left first of all for my wife's place in the country to rest for a whole year. From here I exchanged letters with my old friend Nadezhda Fedorovna Schneyder. She (at that time already a widow) was married to a professor of histology, Bredikhin (brother of the well-known astronomer), she had connections in the university and could furnish me with correct information how far my intention of being a Privatdocent in the university could displease some of the professors. I received an answer that they were not in sympathy with my move. To this I asked them to be reassured that I would not hinder anyone or get in anyone's way. Then I received a satisfactory answer, and in early spring I went to Moscow to submit my application for the position of Privatdocent. I went to the dean's and the rector's (the physiologist Ivanov), but did not find either of them at home; the rector's servant declared to me that he very much loved bishop's service and would be in it. Only the trustee, Count Kapnist, received me, and very amiably, remarking by the way, that according to the new regulations there was no need for me to retire, which I did not know and which they did not tell me in Petersburg. Upon my arrival in Moscow I met friendly interest on the part of the young professor of comparative anatomy, kind, good Mikhail Aleks. Menzbir. In his own small accommodations he gave me a separate room, and I spent a whole year here.

Not having available any instruments except the absorptiometer, a knife and an induction apparatus and not wishing to hamper the physiological laboratory, I decided to lecture on a section of physiology which did not require complex instrument supplies, namely, the central nervous system. The fruit of this was *Physiology of the Nervous System*, which I published in Moscow. The authorities did not honor my first lecture with a visit, for some reason; there were rather many students at the lectures, but I only received 60 rubles for my fee.

This same year I was invited to give lectures to medical students on the premises of their club along Bolshoy Dmitrovka. So many attended and the fee was so great that the thought came to me to establish a small laboratory in Moscow. The trustee promised to give me a small room, and I, when the academic year had expired, went abroad to buy instruments, and was in Paris for this purpose. On this very trip I tried, thanks to Ducleau, to arouse the interest of the French in my work with CO_2, to which I referred above. On the way back to Russia I stopped in Leipzig at my dear teacher, Ludwig's. In view of the vagueness of my position at that time he without any provocation on my part told me not to forget that while he was alive, there would always be a room for me in his laboratory. When I returned to Russia I found out, with great grief, that there was not the room promised me, and I almost decided mentally to work abroad at Ludwig's, and only to gives lectures in Moscow. I stayed during the end of the summer at my wife's in the country with these thoughts, and suddenly I received a telegram from the trustee in which it was mentioned that by chance of professor of physiology Sheremet'yevskiy's unexpected death, the medical department and he, the trustee, suggested that I occupy this chair. The knowledge that in this place I could be of more use to the medical department than as a Privatdocent without a corner to work compelled me to accept the suggestion, and in the following 10 years of professorship (1891-1901) I never had occasion to regret this decision: my colleagues in the medical department gave me a hearty welcome; in the laboratory, in the person of my closest co-worker, Lev Zakharovich Morokhovets I found such an amicable friend that during the whole 10 years I did not once feel like a newcomer in a strange nest; finally, among the students I had the luck to find a friend, M. N. Shaternikov, with whom it was a great delight for me to work, the more so since we worked not without success. Still during the year of my position as a Privatdocent I met a disposition friendly and extremely valuable to me on the part of such people as Kliment Arkad'yevich Timiryazev and Professor Stoletov, and later I became intimate with Aleksandr Ivanovich Chuprov and Nikolay Il'ich Storozhenko. Must I say that under such circumstances life flowed peacefully and pleasantly. And later, the passage from Odessa to Moscow joined the friends Nikolay Aleksandrovich and Yelena Leonardovna Umova to all the others. She, even to the present time, has remained a friend to me, immediately after my first unfailing friend— my wife.

When I received the chair of physiology, L. Z. Morokhovets was the dissector for it, according to the new regulations, and my first business was to obtain for him the title of professor extraordinarius. After this it was now easy for us to share our work in the department amicably, as two members enjoying equal rights. He possessed great talents of economy, of which I was deprived; therefore, the management of the institute was left to him, the more so since he was the organizer of the physiological institute; the greater number of lectures were left to me as the more experienced lecturer (I had four hours a week, and he had two). I obtained two rooms on the lower floor at my complete disposal and settled in them in a most pleasant way with my co-worker Mikhail Nikolayevich Shaternikov. I am indebted to Lev Zakharovich's tact and friendship for the fact that, having 10 years of professorship peacefully in these rooms, I am peacefully in them even now, having retired. What fortune this is can be understood only by one who, like me, has spent almost half a century in the laboratory (since 1856) and is no longer capable of another sort of existence.

Also, acquaintance with women's courses in the society of women educators and teachers, where I was invited to give lectures, brought me no small comfort. And here, as in the friendly family of Nadezhda Vasil'yevna Stasova of Bestuzhev times, that freedom and ease connected with decency was felt which is given to a family only by the education of its members, decency of goals pursued by the family, and loving relations of the elders to the young ones. The past recalled in this environment is gratifying; at the lectures before my eyes again sat the Bestuzhevs unselfishly striving for knowledge, with the strained attention so familiar to me on their faces. Even a similarity to the unforgettable Nadezhda Vasil'yevna Stasova was not lacking in the face of the manager of the courses, Anna Nikolayevna Sheremet'yevskaya, much younger than Nadezhda Vasil'yevna, but just as good and energetic in every good deed. This institution had a good aim— to give women the opportunity of enriching their education by teaching and preparing to teach; it did not cost the government a penny, did not demand any rights for those who attended, and existed by itself for years peacefully, but did not profit by organized government supervision (i.e., by the fundamental director and his assistants with salary), and was therefore closed as soon as higher courses of Ger'ye came up. Our self-government was in general not in vogue.

I experienced not a few good moments, apart from the friendly society with my colleagues, also in the laboratory of Moscow University. In the very first year of my professorship, my torments because of the fate of my work with CO_2 came to an end. Fate, as if took pity on me, bringing the thought to my mind of testing whether the law I discovered of the solution of a gas in volume-diluted salt solutions would not prove to be correct if instead of CO_2 one dissolves in salt solutions a salt indifferent to the salt of the solvent. With this purpose I began to search in the literature on this question for cases where the solvent would be diluted, as in my experiments with CO_2, in a volume relation. I found such a case in the investigation of Bodländer,[9] and it remained only for me to place the data of his experiments under the formula $y = \alpha l - \dfrac{K}{x}$ to be convinced of the applicability of the law to the solution of salts in salt solutions.

A little later the Moscow chemist Yakobkin corroborated this result in a more general form by his investigations.[10] Thus, I obtained the universal key to a wide class of phenomena after all.

Until this time I had always worked by myself, but as soon as I had a possible co-worker in the student Shaternikov, of good temper, with a good head and skillful hands, I began to work with him. Our first work was the arrangement of an accessory for the manometer of my absorptiometer, for

---

[9] Ueber die Löslichkeit von Salzgemischen im Wasser. *Zeitschr. f. Physikal. Chem.*, Bd. VII, Heft 4.

[10] A. A. Yakobkin. Distribution of substances between two solvents in application to the study of phenomena of chemical statics. *Scientific Notes of Mosc. Univ. Dept. of Nat. Hist.*, no. 12, 1896.

rapid, accurate and recapitulative analysis of atmospheric air.[11] The advantages of this method over the usual eudiometric method, apart from speed, consisted in the calculating of the gas volumes produced under water and the elimination of the mistake of moistening the eudiometer walls with an alkaline solution so that in both volumes of the manometer the columns of alkaline solution filled to an equal height.

In the second general job the plan and some details of the apparatus belong to me; all the rest and the putting of the apparatus into action was his work.[12]

The basic point of the new method of measuring for man the volume of air exhaled and the quantity of CO_2 contained in it consisted of the following. If an unknown volume of exhaled air, x, passing through a system of tubes, meets an alkaline solution and loses in it by absorption a measurable volume, A, of carbonic acid, then the volume x-A will go beyond the limits of the alkaline solution. If, in this, the percentage of carbonic acid (a) in the exhaled air before its passing through the alkaline solution is known, and the corresponding percentage (b) is beyond its limit, then the whole quantity of expired CO_2 will be $\dfrac{ax}{100}$, and the quantity remaining after absorption by the alkaline solution $\dfrac{(x - A)b}{100}$.

Hence $\dfrac{(x - A)b}{100} + A = \dfrac{ax}{100}$, and $x = A \dfrac{100 - b}{a - b}$ (1).

Together with this it of course becomes certain also that the quantity of expired CO_2 is ($\dfrac{ax}{100}$). If, finally, the percentages of O_2 in the inspired and expired air are known, then assuming the volumes of inspired and expired air are equal to each other, an approximately true determination of the quantity of oxygen consumed results.[13]

From the formula it is immediately apparent that the suitability of the method demands: 1) very exact determination of the quantity of carbonic acid absorbed by the alkaline solution because A is multiplied by 100 even in the

---

[11] M. Schaternikoff and J. Setschenow. Ein Beitrag zur Gasanalyse. *Zeitschr. f. physik. Chemie*, XVIII, 4, 1895.

[12] M. N. Shaternikov. New method of determining for man the quantities of air exhaled and the CO_2 contained in it. Moscow, 1899.

[13] A more exact determination of this quantity is received with the nitrogen of the expired air. Since during respiration the quantity of nitrogen remains unchanged, consequently, once the volume of the expired air and the percentage content in it of nitrogen are determined, then also the quantity of it in the inspired air is known; this quantity when multiplied by 21/79 gives the content of O_2 in the inspired air. Thus, if the volume of expired air is V and c is the percent of nitrogen in it, then $\dfrac{V}{100}$. 21/79 will be the volume of oxygen.

case when the whole alkaline solution would be analyzed for absorbing gas; 2) very exact determination of both percentages of carbonic acid, a and b, and 3) so great an absorption of CO_2 by the alkaline solution that the denominator exceeded one or was at least equal to it. Besides the last condition, the absorbent of CO_2 had to show as little resistance as possible to the flow of expired air.

The last two conditions were met by the structure of the absorbent in the form of a low, wide Wolff bottle (with a tube going out at the bottom), an entering tube which was terminated at the lower end, submerged in an alkaline solution, by a wide, flat cylinder, with a great number of openings on the side surface and on the bottom. The dimensions of the bottle and cylinder were calculated so that the layer of alkaline solution required for the experiment above the openings leaving the cylinder did not exceed one cm. Thus, the resistance on the part of the liquid to the flow of air did not exceed 20 mm of water (the manometer showed this, placed before the absorbent). A thick metal grid was placed under the alkaline solution, opposite the splashing of it by the air escaping from the openings. Later, this absorbent was significantly improved by Shaternikov.

Parts of the expired air were withdrawn, for analysis for CO_2, from the main path simultaneously and uniformly on both sides of the absorbent during the whole progress of the experiment. The simultaneity was achieved by mercury, filling the cylinders collecting the gas, flowing from them not directly, but by means of a third cylinder, open from the top, joining them. The uniformity of the flow of mercury out of all three cylinders was achieved by the following simple system. In simple three-ruble clocks, the weight drops uniformly with any length of the pendulum, and the faster, the shorter it is. If, consequently, one connects with the weight of such a clock the free end of a rubber arm leading out of the third cylinder, placing the openings going out of the arm at the same level with the mercury in all the cylinders, then with the motion of the clock together with the flowing out of the mercury from the arm, there will simultaneously be a dropping of the level of mercury in the cylinders—a drop of the outflow opening. So that the mercury in the cylinders dropped with the same speed as the outflow opening (otherwise the dropping of the mercury in the cylinders would not be uniform), there was a stopcock on the path of the mercury in the arm, and by preliminary experiments it was established how much it had to be opened so that the drop in all four places took place with the same speed.

For the determination of A, 1/10 of the whole alkaline solution was taken; the CO_2 absorbed by it was isolated by an acid in a specially constructed apparatus without the least loss, and was measured volumetrically.

To Shaternikov's lot fell the replacement of Zuntz's questionable mouthpiece, with a clamp on the nose, by a very convenient and trustworthy gutta-percha mask, tightly (luftdicht) fitted to the face around the nose and mouth and easily adjusted (by warming the edges of the mask until the gutta-percha is softened) to irregularities of a facial surface of any form. By his labors the form of absorption tube for the volumetric determination of small quantities of CO_2 in large volumes of air was determined. All the parts of the apparatus, the recorder of respiratory movements added to it, and the putting of the mechanism into operation, were managed by him.

Making up the plan of this method, I thought to verify the main result of the experiments—the calculated volume of expired air—by the introduction of a gas clock at the very end of the system; but this apparatus turned out to be unserviceable for the measurement of gas volumes passing through the clock with jerks. Therefore, the method remained unverified until the latest independent work of the already Doctor Shaternikov, produced in 1903-1904.[14]

He had to study the respiration with gas mixtures, great reserves of which collected in the gas meters of known capacity, and through this he achieved the possibility of comparing the volumes of inspired air calculated from the experiment with the volumes actually required and known from the calibrations of the gas meters. Thus, the suitability of the method was demonstrated by Shaternikov.

After the apparatus described for the respiration of a man in a fixed position was arranged, we tried to give it a portable form, giving the opportunity to measure respiration in motion. It is easily understood that this goal could be achieved without difficulty with the help of two light mountings flung over the shoulders from the front to the back with the help of straps. The CO_2 absorbent is fixed on the front mounting, the flat removal bottles (in place of the cylinders) were fixed to the shoulders, and the apparatus with the lowered outflow opening was on the back. A description of the apparatus and the experiments with it were put in L. Z. Morokhovets' journal, *Physiologiste russe*.[15] I confess openly that the arrangement of the portable form was a great joy for me because the investigation of respiration on the move was always a dream of mine which had seemed, besides, unrealizable.

When, at the end of the '80's of the past century news began to come from abroad of the shortening of the time of the working day to 8 hours, without losses for production, the thought came to my mind to investigate a question not before touched, why the heart and respiratory muscles can work unceasingly, but the person, even if he is accustomed to walking, cannot go without

---

[14] M. Schaternikoff, Zur Frage über die abhängigkeit des O_2—Verbrauches von dem O_2—Gehalte in der einzuathmentden Luft. *Engellmann's archiv.* Suppl. Bd., 1904.

[15] Prof. J. Setschenow und Dr. M. Shaternikoff. Ein portativer athmungsapparat. Vol. 11, p. 44, 1900.

tiredness for 27 miles of an uninterrupted way even on a perfectly level road and without any burdening of the body, i.e., under the condition when the work done does not exceed work for the same time (10 hours, counting 2 2/3 miles an hour) of the heart, i.e., of the left ventricle. The reasons for this, I believe, are two: more rapid drainage of the heart of arterial blood and greater duration in it of resting phases of the working muscle, compared with the phases of activity. For the ventricle, at 75 beats a minute the relation between them is like 3 : 5, and during walking, for each foot separately, both phases are approximately equal, as long as the contractions by bending and straightening the leg alternately are equal to each other in duration. From this viewpoint, the inability of the heart and respiratory muscles to fatigue is explained by the fact that minimal fatigue following each contraction has time to become effaced completely in the course of the long rest phases, but during walking, after short rest phases, a complete smoothing out does not take place. The difference in the comparative duration of the phases of activity and rest gives, upon such a glance, the opportunity to calculate how great the additional rest for a ten-hour walk would have to be for its transformation into non-fatiguing work, if the drainage of the leg muscles of arterial blood were as rapid as heart drainage. During 10 hours the entire work of the ventricle (i.e., the sum of all contractions) lasts $3\frac{3}{4}$ hours, and the entire phase of rest $6\frac{1}{4}$ hours; during walking both these quantities were equal to 5 hours. But 5 hours of continuous work of the heart, without fatigue, would demand 8 1/3 hours of rest; consequently, for a 10-hour walk for displacing the fatigue one would have to add 3 1/3 hours of supplementary rest, of course, beyond the 8 hours of sleep which are required also by a non-fatigued person.

I developed these observations in one of my public lectures, and they served later as grounds for my latest laboratory work concerning the inability of the hands to become fatigued during regular periodic work (published in *Physiologiste russe*[16]). I did these experiments on myself, and first of all I had to train my working hand to move with machine regularity (by the beats of a metronome), without participation of the will—just as the feet are moved by habit during walking. Then I found the most useful rate of movements for the working hand and the greatest load under which the heights of its raising remained constant during the course of hours. Thus, I once succeeded in doing 4800 contractions without fatiguing my hand during 4 hours of unbroken work. Then there followed a series of experiments with greater loads, giving clear signs of fatigue (in the form of a gradual diminishing heights to

[16] Prof. J. Setchenow. Zur Frage nach der Einwirkung sensitiver Reize auf die Muskelarbeit des Menschen. Vol. III, 1903.

which the load is raised). Here different forms of rest from fatigue were tested, and among them, to my great surprise, the most effective one turned out to be not the temporary resting of the working hand, but its rest of even shorter duration connected with work of the other hand. It was natural to assume that in this influence temporarily of the working hand on the temporarily resting hand, sensory moments, connected with movement, play a role, and this is confirmed when the stimulating movements were replaced by light tetanization of the hand. The experiments with very large loads, producing fatigue to where moving the hand became impossible, gave the same thing. Thus, the facts found had to be put in the category of long known allies of work—a lively mood, a song, music, etc. Specifically, the facts discovered have, perhaps, the significance of accessories against fatigue during walking and all work in general where different working organs of the body are acting by turns.

My writing activity for this period of time was expressed by three books: *Physiology of Nerve Centers, Essay on the Working Movements of Man,* and a translation from German of F. Noorden's great work.

In the first of these, having the purpose of collecting, with a criticism, everything that had been done of importance in this field, what was new was essentially only an introduction in the treatise—a general survey of nerve phenomena, with the thought underlying it that in the animal body, like a machine, generally all nerve apparatuses have the value of automatic regulators, as, for example, Watt's safety valve in a boiler. This thought was carried through the whole field of phenomena, from reflexes, ensuring the safety of separate organs of the body, to the regulation of all body movements in general in space by indications of the sensory organs. With such a view, the equivalence of generally all the nerve phenomena studied by physiology becomes especially clear; it turns out that the animal mechanism is governed by impulses of two kinds: those arising in the mechanism itself by changes in its motion, and impulses coming from without. Corresponding to this, an organic part of the regulator is the apparatus perceiving the impulse and giving, so to speak, a signal to activity of the motor part, producing the regulation. In regulators operating according to a type of reflexes, the signal parts of the apparatus are distinguished essentially only by the fact that in the most simple apparatuses the signals do not reach the consciousness, in more complex ones they are consciously felt, and in the region of the higher sense organs they are capable even of qualitative alterations.

The circumstance that in the physiological study of the activity of muscles the work aspect of muscle movements is left aside induced me to describe the working movements in man. Corresponding to this, in this small treatise, a description of the element of the working mechanism, i.e., of the bone lever, its axis of rotation, articulations, traction-antagonists, and the nerve apparatus directing the movement made up the main part. In a special part, along with a detailed description of the conditions of movement and stability of various parts of the body, there are works, illustrated by examples, produced by shortenings and lengthenings of the arms and legs, with bending and straightening of the body and others. In this work there are, in my opinion, not a few facts worthy of attention, especially from the aspect of the arrangement of muscle traction in the arms and legs.

By the translation of F. Noorden's medical book I wanted to express in some way my gratitude to the Moscow medical department for sheltering me in old age. In this book, which is very important for clinical physicians, F. Noorden had the great patience and great merit to select from the immense literature (which he cited) all the data on hand concerning the study of the metabolism in a sick person. In view of the circumstance that a comprehensive study of metabolism, forming the only rational way to scientific study of unhealthy states, is possible only for specialists in medical chemistry, and is entirely impossible in those small chemical rooms at clinics, where the investigation of patients' excretions just managed to happen, I had the following thought, which I set forward in the preface to the translation: where the clinics (as in Moscow) are clustered in one spot, do away with the useless chemical rooms found in them for the institution, instead of them, of a central laboratory for all the clinics; build it for the comprehensive study of metabolism, and place a professor of medical chemistry and his assistants at the head of it. This establishment would represent an institute of medical chemistry with two working departments: for the practical studies of students and for chemical-clinical investigations, which would have to be done under the guidance of specialists with clinic assistants. Soon after the printing of the book I had to go abroad, and I did not fail to go to Frankfurt-on-Main to Noorden to seek his advice concerning my plan. He, of course, approved of it and advised me to apply with him by letter to the leading German clinical physicians to find out their opinion. I received a very sympathetic answer from a Berlin professor of a hospital clinic, from Leyden—one a little evasive, with a description not pertaining to the matter of the importance of bacteriological investigation, and from the Munich clinic I did not receive any answer. I sent my plan with the opinion of Noorden and both of the clinical physicians mentioned to the ministry of education and to the rector of Odessa University, the physicist Shvedov, since they were building clinics at that time at Odessa. The answer from Shvedov was sympathetic; nevertheless, my plan vanished without a trace.

My project of change of examinations for the degree of doctor of medicine, presented in answer to the circular proposal of the ministry to discuss this question in the departments, was as unsuccessful. I remember that the main points of this project were the following: the graduate student for the doctor's degree had to write and defend his thesis in illustration of the specialty he had chosen first, and only then take the examination—general background for all doctors in general, in physics, chemistry, anatomy, physiology and microscopy, and a special one on the subject he chose. One Fedor Fedorovich Erismann signed this project; it was rejected by all the remaining members of the department.

I cannot help recalling in this case the sad fact of Professor Erismann's removal, by the will of the higher authorities, from Moscow University. This man had very great value for our fatherland. Before him, hygiene existed in Russia only nominally, but in his hands it started with an active beginning against many general shortcomings and evils. He founded a *really working* hygienic institute, which served not only science, but also society. He did so much for zemstvo medicine that among zemstvo doctors his name is placed along side S. P. Botkin's name, according to merits, and is justly placed there. Working indefatigably, he was an excellent professor and found time to write a textbook on hygiene which was vast and very valuable to the specialists. The reason why he was removed has remained unknown, but of course it was because of the theory of suspicion which governs us even in these times, which (i.e., suspicion), in the words of Count Delyanov to Erismann's wife (and also to the well-known lawyer, Dril') is sensed by the authorities with the nose. I knew Erismann for more than 25 years; we were friends of his; he did not hide from me either his views or his convictions, and I can testify by my conscience that he was not a man of extreme opinions. For us who knew Erismann from the time of his arrival in Russia, it was all the more striking in him that he turned from a Swiss into a Russian, sincerely loved Russia, and devoted all the best years of his life in her service.

Is it not sad that that very same hand (Mr. Delyanov's) which removed a deserved man, sat, nonentities who disgraced the name of professor, on chairs? Will the end to such sad occurrences come sometime?

After this unintentional digression I return to my interrupted story about what I wrote in Moscow.

In conclusion I will recall one of the public lectures I gave in Moscow and published then in the *Herald of Europe* entitled "Impressions and Reality." Here I examined the question to what extent does what we see correspond with reality—a question which seems idle at first glance since between sensation and reality lies an abyss. However, this truth does not entirely apply to visual sensations because they are objectivized, i.e. they are brought out in the form of a definite figure of a definite size, of a definite distance from the eye, and with a definite coloring. Consequently, in relation to visual impressions the problem arises as to how far one or another aspect of the objectivized sensation coincides with reality. In regard to the flat face of objects, how far can it be outlined in lines, the problem is solved in the following way.

Although we receive only sensory signs from external objects, nevertheless continual experiment proves in unquestionable form that the identity or likeness of the external influences producing them always correspond to the identity or likeness of the signs perceived. If, therefore, the plane face of an object and its image on the retina are similar to each other and the image on the retina is similar to the corresponding objectivized sensation, then the latter is similar to the plane face of the object.

The first of these propositions does not require proof: the likeness between images on the retina and objectivized sensations is all the more clearly proven by light diffusion in the eye where what is seen *deviating from reality, coincides with what is pictured on the retina*. Thus, the external object appears to us with moving contours, if its image moves on the retina; a fluorescent dot is seen bifurcated, in the form of a triangle, a cross, and other forms, if we place in front of the eye a screen with holes cut out of it which do not exceed the size of the pupil, in the form of two openings, a triangle, a cross, and other forms. This happens immediately, when the eye is not adjusted to the distance of the fluorescent dot; but then also on the retina are pictured dispersed images in the form of two dots, a triangle, a cross, and other forms. And what other meaning could the presence in the eye of the human and many animals of a refracting medium, which provides plane images of external objects, have?

I did work with conditions of fatigue and rest, after I had already retired, using my former accommodations in the laboratory, thanks to the sincerely friendly regard for me by the laboratory director, L. Z. Morokhovets. I was prompted to put an end to my teaching activity by my years, by my consciousness of the backwardness which had set in in science, and by my conviction that an old man ought not wait for the time when the public will wish for his resignation. My resignation, it is true, did not provoke regrets either in the authorities or in my listeners; but on the other hand, there were also no indications that my resignation was desirable. My petition of retirement was served by me in the beginning of the academic year, and for about three months I did not know anything about its fate. Thinking that it had become stuck at some department from the office of the university to the office of the ministry, I went with a question about this to the rector and found out, to my great surprise, that my business could be finished in several days: at the ring of a bell, an official from the office appeared, the rector charged him to write down my service list, and the matter was concluded without further conversations.

But this was not yet the end of my teaching activity; its real end was ahead.

In Moscow, in the technical society, there are the so-called Prechistenskiy courses for workers, at which, among other things, lectures on natural science, and also anatomy and physiology are given. When I first heard about this institution, I thought that the popularization of scientific knowledge was led to extreme limits in these courses, and was very surprised that the chemistry given there did not yield to popularization, and besides it was given by such a serious person as the well-known Moscow chemist Mikhail Ivanovich Konovalov (later professor of chemistry in Kiev polytechnic school). To disperse my doubts, I was invited by a listener to one of his lectures. I never in my life heard such a skillful adaptation of a serious reading to the intellectual means of an audience. The course obviously was planned and was carried out so that each step forward had a basis in one of the immediately preceding ones. Making such a step, the lecturer turned to the audience with the question of what served as a basis for this step, and each time the right answer was heard from the audience. With this, I must remark that Mikhail Ivanovich's lecture did not differ at all in content from the lectures given to university students. A strong impression was received also from the audience, which listened with a certain greed to the simple and clear speech of its professor, which was reinforced at every step by an experiment. I was imbued with even greater respect for this audience when I learned that many workers run to these lectures at the end of their evening work at the factory from Butyrskiy gates; many studied foreign languages—some even English. God preserve and expand this sympathetic institution—the prototype of a people's university.

In the beginning of the last academic year they invited me to lecture on anatomy and physiology at the Prechistenskiy courses, and I accepted the offer, feeling that I was backward for lecturing at the university but still fit to give elementary courses, the more so since my faithful friend and co-worker, Shaternikov, undertook to assist at these lectures. And my audience produced on me a gratifying impression with its attention and its evident understanding of what I gave. From October through February I succeeded in giving the structure and mobility of the skeleton with the laws of distribution of attachments and traction, the anatomy and physiology of external integuments, the digestive organs, circulation of the blood, and respiration; all that remained was the lecturing on muscles and a general survey of nerve phenomena, with a more detailed description of vision and hearing. But the lectures had to be stopped after I received the document which I cite below word for word.

IMPERIAL
RUSSIAN TECHNICAL
SOCIETY

MOSCOW SECTION

PERMANENT COMMISSION
ON TECHNICAL
EDUCATION

MOSCOW
February 9, 1904, No. 523

TO THE INSPECTOR
OF PRECHISTENSKIY CLASSES

Letter of the director of people's colleges of February 5, 1904 for No. 814 Professor Ivan Mikhaylovich Sechenov is not approved in the post of teacher of Prechistenskiy classes, and therefore kindly notify me of his release from employment.

Chairman K. MAZING

Thus, my teaching activity came to an end.